Verse and Prose
Anthology

Volume 17

The LAMDA Verse and Prose Anthology (Volume 17)
first published in 2009 by the
London Academy of Music and Dramatic Art
155 Talgarth Road, London W14 9DA
Tel: 0844 847 0520 / Fax: 0844 847 0521
e-mail: publications@lamda.org.uk
www.lamda.org.uk

Edited by Greg Hamerton

A catalogue record for this book is available from the British
Library.

Printed by Athenaeum Press.

Cover image: The handwriting of Thomas Hardy, from an
original manuscript.

ISBN 978-0-9557687-2-9

Contents

Introduction

LAMDA has kept alive the tradition of speaking, reciting and performing poetry. Nearly all poems sit on the page inviting us to turn them into sounds. The ways in which the words make rhythms and chime with each other is something that not only pleases the ear but also plays with our feelings. One moment we might be lulled, another made sorrowful, another led towards something joyous. Pauses between words and lines can become moments for reflection or suspense.

Poems are one of the best ways in which we can say big things in small spaces, and because they have these musical qualities they also become ways in which we can carry these big things in our head: memorable philosophy, you could call it.

So best of luck to anyone and everyone reading, performing and listening to the poems in this anthology and I hope that you will all find ways to enjoy poetry whenever you need to.

Michael Rosen

UK Children's Laureate (2007–2009)

Thanks

We are grateful to the many authors and publishers who have granted us permission to reproduce their work and to the following who contributed to the development of the anthology: Mia Ball, Wendy Daniels, Brian Hindle and Julia Watson.

INTRODUCTORY

Lions and Tigers

The lion roars, the tiger growls,
Their mouths are open wide,
Then, suddenly, they snap them closed,
To trap their prey inside.
They chew their food with strong, white teeth
Which sparkle when they smile,
They lick their lips with long, pink tongues
Then yawn, and sleep awhile.

by A Nightingale

Before the Bath

It's cold, cold, cold
And the water shines wet,
And the longer I wait
The colder I get.

I can't quite make
Myself hop in
All shivery-cold
In just my skin.

Yet the water's warm
In the tub, I know
So – one, two, three,
And IN I go!

by Corinna Marsh

When the Giant Comes to Breakfast

When the giant comes to breakfast,
He eats cornflakes with a spade,
Followed by a lorry-load
Of toast and marmalade.

Next, he takes a dustbin,
Fills it up with tea,
Drinks it all in a gulp
And leaves the mess for me.

by John Coldwell

Tastes

Jelly's slippery.

Ice-cream's cold.

Toffee's sweet
And sticky to hold.

Curry is hot
And full of spice.

Crisps are crunchy.

Chocolate's nice.

by John Foster

Ask Mummy Ask Daddy

When I ask Daddy
Daddy says ask Mummy.

When I ask Mummy
Mummy says ask Daddy.
I don't know where to go.

Better ask my teddy
He never says no.

by John Agard

Tailpiece

Tongues we use for talking.
Hands we clasp and link.
Feet are meant for walking.
Heads are where we think.
Toes are what we wiggle.
Knees are what we bend.
Then there's what we sit on
And that's about the end.

by Max Fatchen

GROUP INTRODUCTORY

Dinosaur Roar!

Dinosaur roar, dinosaur squeak,
Dinosaur fierce, dinosaur meek,
Dinosaur fast, dinosaur slow,
Dinosaur above and dinosaur below.
Dinosaur weak, dinosaur strong,
Dinosaur short, or very, very long.
Dinosaur fat, dinosaur tiny,
Dinosaur clean and dinosaur slimy.
Dinosaur sweet, dinosaur grumpy,
Dinosaur spiky and dinosaur lumpy.
All sorts of dinosaurs eating up their lunch,
Gobble, gobble, nibble, nibble,
MUNCH... MUNCH... SCRUNCH!

by Henrietta Stickland

There Are Big Waves

There are big waves and little waves,
    Green waves and blue,
Waves you can jump over,
    Waves you dive thro',
Waves that rise up
    Like a great water wall,
Waves that swell softly
    And don't break at all,
Waves that can whisper,
    Waves that can roar,
And tiny waves that run at you
    Running on the shore.

by Eleanor Farjeon

Elephant Antics

One little elephant
sitting on a bunk.
Along came another one
and pulled his trunk!

Two little elephants
in a tug-of-war.
Two more joined in
and then there were four.

Four *more* came along,
so there were eight
pulling and tugging
with all their weight.

They all fell over.
And guess what happened then.
They jumped up
and started all over again.

by Jill Townsend

PREPARATORY

Tarantula

She's hairy,
She's scary,
She's covered in bristles.
A fighter,
A biter,
With legs like eight thistles.

A muncher,
A cruncher,
With greedy jaws gnashing.
A mawler,
A crawler...

But I think she's SMASHING!

by Clare Bevan

Sock Song

Upstairs
Downstairs
Where can they be?
I can't find my socks
and they can't find me!

Bedroom
Bathroom
Where have they gone?
I can't find my socks
and I need to put them on!

Inside
Outside
Hanging on the line?
I can't find my socks

and I'm running out of time!

One sock
Two socks
Silly things to lose
and when I've found my socks...

I'll be hunting for my shoes!

by Ian McMillan

The Answers

"When did the world begin and how?"
I asked a lamb,
   a goat,
      a cow.
"What is it all about and why?"
I asked a hog as he went by.
"Where will the whole thing end and when?"
I asked a duck,
   a goose
      a hen:
And I copied all the answers too,
A quack
   a honk
      an oink
         a moo.

by Robert Clairmont

The Ugstabuggle

Over by my bedroom wall
The ugstabuggle stands,
A monster nearly nine feet tall
With hairy, grasping hands.
In afternoons and mornings
He's always out of sight,
But often I can see him
In the darkness late at night.
Yet when I do not think of him
He disappears again,
And when I sleep he goes, because
I cannot see him then!

by Peter Wesley-Smith

Stripey Tiger

A tiger has stripes
From its head to its tail,
A polar bear hasn't,
Nor has a whale.

A panda is patchy,
A leopard has spots,
A giraffe's sort of blotchy,
A deer has white dots.

An elephant's grey
And a fox is all red,
But a tiger has stripes
From his tail to his head.

by Daphne Lister

Footprints

I left my footprints on the sand
    and watched them follow me,
For every place that I had gone
    I saw them by the sea.
But when the tide came in, it washed
    my footprints all away
And left no trace of them upon
    the sand I trod today.

by John Travers Moore

GROUP PREPARATORY

Jungle Piece

Down in the jungle
Late at night,
Whisp'ring voices
Take to flight –
Monkeys chatter,
Parrots squawk,
Snakes are hissing,
Tribe drums talk.
Down in the jungle,
Shadows creep,
Through the long grass
Bright eyes peep.
Lions are lurking,
Leopards stall –
Listen – hard!
That's Tarzan's call!
Aaooooooooooooooow!

by Jacqueline Emery

Funny the Way Different Cars Start

Funny the way
Different cars start.
Some with a chunk and a jerk,
Some with a cough and a puff of smoke
Out of the back,
Some with only a little click –
                with hardly any noise.

Funny the way
Different cars run.
Some rattle and bang,
Some whirr
Some knock and knock.

Some purr
And hummmmm
Smoothly on
　　　　with hardly any noise.

by Dorothy Baruch

The Small Ghostie

When it's late and it's dark
And everyone sleeps... shhh shhh shhh,
Into our kitchen
A small ghostie creeps... shhh shhh shhh.

We hear knocking and raps
And then rattles and taps,

Then he clatters and clangs
And he batters and bangs,

And he whistles and yowls
And he screeches and howls...

So we pull up our covers over our heads
And we block up our ears and WE STAY IN OUR BEDS.

by Barbara Ireson

PRELIMINARY

Yuck

Jam all over her fingers,
Pastry in her hair,
Fruit juice dribbling down her chin
And custard *every*where.

Playdough in her fingernails,
Mud between her toes,
And something much much nastier
Running from her nose.

But none of that would bother me
If it weren't for this:
My sister's heading this way fast –
And it's *me* she wants to kiss!

by Paul Rogers

Story Time

When our teacher tells us stories
at the end of every day,
we all sit in silence
as she takes us far away.

To places where wise wizards
live in castles in the sky,
to lands where all the children
have wings so they can fly.

We all sit in silence
we just sit and stare,
for when teacher tells us stories
she makes us feel we're there.

by Andrew Collett

Star-trip

Where is it mermaids swim in the sea?
Where is it unicorns roam about free?
Is there a planet where dragons are found
And witches on broomsticks still hover around?
Is there a planet where giants and gnomes
And spell-making wizards have all made their homes?

I'm going to find it, perhaps it's not far,
So start up the engines and head for that star.

by Barbara Ireson

The Babysitter

It was clear
From the moment
They walked out the door
That Tracey
Had never done
This job before.

Until they came home
She patiently sat
On me
        my little brother
                and the cat.

by Lindsay MacRae

Going Swimming

Kick off your shoes, pull off your clothes,
The pool smell tingles up your nose.

That shower is freezing – shiver, shout –
Leap in the water, splash about.

Doggy paddle, slip and slop,
Jump and dive and belly flop.

Splosh the breaststroke, plunge the crawl,
Float on your back, and throw a ball.

Before you know an hour's gone by –
Another shower – a brisk rub dry.

And then the best part of the treat –
A bag of fish and chips to eat.

by Alison Chisholm

Grown Out Of

My trousers are tight.
They just won't fit.

And my jumper?
I've grown out of it.

My shirt's too short.
It just won't do.

There are holes in my socks
where my toes peep through.

So it's lucky I don't
grow out of my skin.

'Cos then there'd be nothing
to put *me* in.

by Tony Mitton

GROUP PRELIMINARY

Remember

Remember when
the world was tall
and you were small
and legs were all
you saw?

Thin legs
fat legs
dog legs
cat legs.

Table legs
chair legs
dark legs
fair legs.

Quick legs
slow legs
nowhere-
to-go legs.

Jumping legs
prancing legs
skipping legs
dancing legs.

Shoes-and-sock legs
on the rocks legs.

Standing-very-tall legs
running-all-around legs.

Stooping-very-small legs
lying-on-the-ground legs.

Remember when
the world was tall
and you were small
and legs were all
you saw?

by Pamela Mordecai

Skeleton House

Push, push the heavy door
CREE...CREE...CREEEEK!
Tip-toe the rotten floor
SQUEE...SQUEEE...SQUEEEEK!
Step across the missing stair
EER...EEER...EEEERK!
Is that something over there?
SWISH...SWISH...SWISH...
Behind the curtain, what is that?
SCRITTER...SCRITTER...BUMP!
A red-eyed rat, a swooping bat
OOOW...OOOOOW...OOOOOW!
There's something sitting in that chair
SSH...SSSH...SSSSH!
His head is white with cobweb hair
OH!...NO!...SSH!
He starts to speak with clacking jaws
CLACK...CLACK...CLACK!
I grab his leg with all my force
PULL...PULL.....PULL.....PULL..
Just like I'm pulling yours!

by Lawrence Smith

Storm

Heavy air,
Phew it's warm,
Think we'll get
A thunderstorm,
Sky grows black,
Inky clouds,
Distant rumblings
Getting loud.
There's a flash,
Now it comes,
Thunder beats
On Heaven's drums,
And another,
Forked and bright,
Clap so loud,
What a fright!
Windows rattle
Dog is scared,
Here's another,
Be prepared!
Easing off now,
Spots of rain,
Hope that storm
Won't come again.

by Eleanor McLeod

ENTRY

Lizard

A flash of green,
a flicker of light,
a gleam of gold
   glittering
just out of sight.

    A heat-hazed wall,
    a wreath of vine,
    a glint of eye
       blinking
    in bright sunshine.

        A zap of speed,
        a glimmer of jade,
        a hint of movement
           diving
        deep into shade.

by Moira Andrew

The Magic Cat

My mum whilst walking through the door
spilt some magic on the floor.
Blobs of this
and splots of that
but most of it upon the cat.

Our cat turned magic, straight away
and in the garden went to play
where it grew two massive wings
and flew around in fancy rings.
"Oh look!" cried Mother, pointing high,
"I didn't know our cat could fly."
Then with a dash of Tibby's tail
she turned my mum into a snail!

So now she lives beneath a stone
and dusts around a different home.
And I'm an ant
and Dad's a mouse
and Tibby's living in our house.

by Peter Dixon

Tiptoe

Yesterday I skipped all day,
The day before I ran,
Today I'm going to tiptoe
Everywhere I can.
I'll tiptoe down the stairway.
I'll tiptoe through the door.
I'll tiptoe to the living room
And give an awful roar
And my father, who is reading,
Will jump up from his chair
And mumble something silly like
"I didn't see you there."

I'll tiptoe to my mother
And give a little cough
And when she spins to see me
Why, I'll softly tiptoe off.
I'll tiptoe through the meadows,
Over hills and yellow sands
And when my toes get tired
Then I'll tiptoe on my hands.

by Karla Kuskin

The Wizard Said:

"You find a sheltered spot that faces south..."
    "And then?"
"You sniff and put two fingers in your mouth..."
    "And then?"
"You close your eyes and roll your eye-balls round..."
    "And then?"
"You lift your left foot slowly off the ground..."
    "And then?"
"You make your palm into a kind of cup..."
    "And then?"
"You very quickly raise your right foot up..."
    "And then?"
"You fall over."

by Richard Edwards

Monkey

Have you ever watched a monkey
Climbing up a tree?
He can reach the tip-most top-most
Before you count to three.
And those who try to catch him
Just haven't got a chance.
Off he goes like a man in space
A monkey grin on his monkey face,
Legs and tail all over the place
And lands on another branch.
A cow may moo and a bee may buzz
But none can jump like a monkey does!

by Herbert Kretzmer

Football

Whistle and shout
Bang and shove
Kick and tackle
Run.
Showers of turf
Flying mud
Aim and shoot
Off.
High-scaling ball
Scurrying men
Faster and faster
Leap.
Mad, shrieking crowd,
Tackle and win,
Dribble and shoot
GOAL!

by Jacqueline Emery

Thirst

A long large crocodile lay basking in the sun,
The day was warm,
The sky was blue,
And he was having fun.
But the hot sand tickled him, and his throat was getting dry.
He stretched himself,
He smacked his jaws;
A pool had caught his eye.
The cooling water tempted him, he sidled to the bank,
The water gleamed,
Cold, crystal clear,
So there he stayed and drank.

by H Hancock

Night Sounds

When I lie in bed
I think I can hear
The stars being switched on
I think I can.

And I think I can hear
The moon
Breathing.

But I have to be still.
So still.
All the house is sleeping.
Except for me.

Then I think I can hear it.

by Berlie Doherty

GRADE ONE

Unfair

When we went over the park
Sunday mornings
To play football
We picked sides.

Lizzie was our striker
Because she had the best shot.

When the teachers
Chose the school team
Marshy was our striker.

Lizzie wasn't allowed to play,
They said.

So she watched us lose, instead…

by Michael Rosen

The Eagle

He clasps the crag with crooked hands;
Close to the sun in lonely lands,
Ring'd with the azure world, he stands.

The wrinkled sea beneath him crawls;
He watches from his mountain walls,
And like a thunderbolt he falls.

by Alfred, Lord Tennyson

About the Teeth of Sharks

The thing about a shark is – teeth,
One row above, one row beneath.

Now take a close look. Do you find
It has another row behind?

Still closer – here, I'll hold your hat:
Has it a third row behind that?

Now look in and... Look out! Oh my,
I'll *never* know now! Well, goodbye.

by John Ciardi

Ears

Have you thought to give three cheers
For the usefulness of ears?
Ears will often spring surprises
Coming in such different sizes.
Ears are crinkled, even folded.
Ears turn pink when you are scolded.
Ears can have the oddest habits
Standing rather straight on rabbits.
Ears are little tape-recorders
Catching all the family orders.
Words, according to your mother,
Go in one and out the other.
Each side of your head you'll find them.
Don't forget to wash behind them.
Precious little thanks they'll earn you
Hearing things that don't concern you.

by Max Fatchen

Palanquin Bearers

Lightly, O lightly we bear her along,
She sways like a flower in the wind of our song;
She skims like a bird on the foam of a stream,
She floats like a laugh from the lips of a dream.
Gaily, O gaily we glide and we sing,
We bear her along like a pearl on a string.

Softly, O softly we bear her along,
She hangs like a star in the dew of our song;
She springs like a beam on the brow of the tide,
She falls like a tear from the eyes of a bride.
Lightly, O lightly we glide and we sing,
We bear her along like a pearl on a string.

by Sarojini Naidu

The Sound

A skyful of stars
blinked silent messages.
No moon glistened the leaves
of the sleeping jungle
where a thousand small creatures
curled at rest.

Then... the Sound –
huge as mountains
it cracked the stillness,
trampled the forest floor
with its trumpeting...

Elephant!

by Ruth Dalton

House Fear

Always – I tell you this they learned –
Always at night when they returned
To the lonely house from far away,
To lamps unlighted and fire gone gray,
They learned to rattle the lock and key
To give whatever might chance to be,
Warning and time to be off in flight:
And preferring the out- to the indoor night,
They learned to leave the house door wide
Until they had lit the lamp inside.

by Robert Frost

Summing up

A poet came to our school
to earn his daily bread,
a real live poet
with words in his head.
He told us to write a poem
before the lunchtime bell.
We said that we would,
if he would as well.
Some of ours were rather good,
but his face was rather red
because he couldn't do one –
his words were prisoners in his head.
He said he hadn't been inspired –
that's just like me with sums:
I sit and stare at numbers,
but inspiration never comes.

by Nigel Gray

GRADE TWO – VERSE

Escape Plan

As I, Stegosaurus,
stand motionless
in the museum
I am secretly planning
My escape.

At noon
Pterodactyl
will cause a diversion
by wheeling around the museum's
high ceilings
and diving at the curators and
museum staff
while I
quietly slip out of the fire exit
and melt
into the London crowds.

by Roger Stevens

The Computer's Swallowed Grandma

The computer's swallowed grandma
Yes 'honestly' it's true.
She pressed 'control' and 'enter'
And disappeared from view.

It's devoured her completely
The thought just makes me squirm.
Maybe she's caught a virus
Or been eaten by a worm.

I've searched through the recycle bin
And files of every kind.
I've even used the Internet
But nothing did I find.

In desperation I asked Jeeves
My searches to refine.
The reply from him was negative
Not a thing was found 'online'.

So, if inside your 'inbox'
My Grandma you should see.
Please 'scan', 'copy' and 'paste' her
In an e-mail back to me.

by Valerie Waite

The Song of Hiawatha (Hiawatha's Brothers)

Then the little Hiawatha
Learned of every bird its language,
Learned their names and all their secrets,
How they built their nests in Summer,
Where they hid themselves in Winter,
Talked with them whene'er he met them,
Called them 'Hiawatha's Chickens'.

Of all beasts he learned the language,
Learned their names and all their secrets,
How the beavers built their lodges,
Where the squirrels hid their acorns,
How the reindeer ran so swiftly,
Why the rabbit was so timid,
Talked with them whene'er he met them,
Called them 'Hiawatha's Brothers'.

by Henry Wadsworth Longfellow

A Fierce Pirate Crew

We are a fierce pirate crew, with cutlasses in hand,
Known throughout the Seven Seas as a bold, bloodthirsty
    band;
From the sands of Timbuctoo to the east of Samarkand,
Our death-defying deeds are known on sea or on the land.

Our galleon named the Dirty Dick is sturdy stout and strong,
With great black sails a-billowing wide as we sail along,
She dips and heaves and plunges tall grey foaming waves
    among
And as the evening darkens we speed her with a song,

Singing: "Heave away me hearties, our daily plundering's
    done,
Heave away me hearties here's a fine old bottle of rum!"
We'll sit and tell bold tales until we see the morning sun
Then look out all you jolly tars, for here the pirates come!

With the cry of "Pirate galley!" the bravest Captain's eyes
Are filled with the greatest horror as the Dirty Dick he spies,
For soon along the quivering plank his gallant crew all dies.
Treachery is on the sea when the Jolly Roger flies.

by Eleanor McLeod

Twilight

Don't say I didn't tell you
about those creepy noises in the dark wood;
I heard them clearly where alone I stood
for a moment under the staring trees there
disturbing the silent air.

It was only owls.

Don't say I didn't warn you
about those spooky lights on the green pool;
I saw them plainly coming home from school
for a moment just beyond the town
dancing up and down.

It was only stars.

by Leonard Clark

The Witch's Brew

Into my pot there now must go
Leg of lamb and green frog's toe,
Old men's socks and dirty jeans,
A rotten egg and cold baked beans.
　　Hubble bubble at the double
　　Cooking pot stir up some trouble.
One dead fly and a wild wasp's sting,
The eye of a sheep and the heart of a king.
A stolen jewel and mouldy salt,
And for good flavour a jar of malt.
　　Hubble bubble at the double
　　Cooking pot stir up some trouble.
Wing of bird and head of mouse,
Screams and howls from a haunted house.
And don't forget the pint of blood,
Or the sardine tin and the clod of mud.
　　Hubble bubble at the double
　　Cooking pot stir up some TROUBLE!

by Wes Magee

Amanda!

Don't bite your nails, Amanda!
Don't hunch your shoulders, Amanda!
Stop that slouching and sit up straight,
Amanda!

(There is a languid, emerald sea,
where the sole inhabitant is me –
a mermaid, drifting blissfully.)

Did you finish your homework, Amanda?
Did you tidy your room, Amanda?
I thought I told you to clean your shoes,
Amanda!

(I am an orphan, roaming the street.
I pattern soft dust with my hushed, bare feet.
The silence is golden, the freedom is sweet.)

Don't eat that chocolate, Amanda!
Remember your acne, Amanda!
Will you please look at me when I'm speaking to you,
Amanda!

(I am Rapunzel, I have not a care;
life in a tower is tranquil and rare;
I'll certainly *never* let down my bright hair!)

Stop that sulking at once, Amanda!
You're always so moody, Amanda!
Anyone would think that I nagged at you,
Amanda!

by Robin Klein

The Sound Collector

A stranger called this morning
Dressed all in black and grey
Put every sound into a bag
And carried them away.

The whistling of the kettle
The turning of the lock
The purring of the kitten
The ticking of the clock

The popping of the toaster
The crunching of the flakes
When you spread the marmalade
The scraping noise it makes

The hissing of the frying-pan
The ticking of the grill
The bubbling of the bathtub
As it starts to fill

The drumming of the raindrops
On the window-pane
When you do the washing-up
The gurgle of the drain

The crying of the baby
The squeaking of the chair
The swishing of the curtain
The creaking of the stair

A stranger called this morning
He didn't leave his name
Left us only silence
Life will never be the same.

by Roger McGough

GRADE TWO – PROSE

Spid

First one leg came out of the plughole and then another, and then another and then another and then another and then another and then another and then another.

Spid had arrived.

"I thought spiders only had six legs," said the boy who was looking over the edge of the bath, "but I've been counting yours and I thought they would never stop. You are the biggest spider I have ever seen! Are you sure you only have *eight* legs? You haven't left any down there? Where do you come from, anyway?"

The spider explained that he had been trying to get into the house for some weeks, because hiding in a coalshed was not his idea of happiness. He loved people, he said, and he wanted people to love him too.

"*I* love spiders," said the boy, "but nobody else does, not in this house! My mother screams when she sees one. My father stamps on them!"

"Ouch!" exclaimed the spider, twitching its feet.

"I know," the boy agreed, "but that is why you can't come to live here, I'm afraid. Besides, my grandmother is coming to stay, and she feels faint if she even catches sight of a spider, and our lady helper catches them in dusters and shakes them out of the window."

"Aiee!" said the spider, bunching itself into a ball.

"My Aunty Bloss traps them in a toothglass and puts them in the boiler," continued the boy. "You do see why you can't come and live here, don't you?"

by Ursula Moray Williams

Harry's Mad

Harry jumped out of bed, put on his dressing-gown, opened the door and (for once) went down the stairs very slowly and quietly. Closing the sitting-room door behind him, he went over to the parrot-cage and stood beside it. It was on a level with his head.

Harry put on his sneering Gestapo interrogator face.

"Ve haf vays of making you talk!" he said between clenched teeth.

The parrot said nothing.

Harry took a deep breath. A hundred times, he said to himself, I'll say it a hundred times. He leaned forward till his lips were almost against the wire bars of the cage, as close as possible to where he thought the bird's ear must be, and, speaking slowly and clearly, as you would to a foreigner or to someone rather deaf, he said, "*My... name... is... Madison.*"

The parrot scratched the side of his bare, scaly face with one foot.

"If you say so, buddy," he said clearly, "but that would be a remarkable coincidence. Seeing that my name is Madison also."

Harry's mouth fell open. He felt amazement, embarrassment, wild excitement, all at the same time.

"What's the matter?" said Madison pleasantly. "Cat got your tongue?"

by Dick King-Smith

A Handful of Horrid Henry

It was showtime.

Horrid Henry was not very excited.

He did not want to be a raindrop.

And he certainly did not want to be a raindrop who danced behind a giant green leaf.

Miss Thumper waddled over to the piano. She banged on the keys.

The curtain went up.

I'm not staying back here, he thought, and pushed his way through the raindrops.

"Stop pushing, Henry!" hissed Lazy Linda.

Henry pushed harder, then did a few pitter-pats with the other raindrops.

Miss Tutu stretched out a bony arm and yanked Henry back behind the scenery.

Who wants to be a raindrop anyway, thought Henry. I can do what I like hidden here.

Henry flapped his arms and pretended he was a *pterodactyl* about to pounce on Miss Tutu.

Round and round he flew, homing in on his prey.

Perfect Peter stepped to the front and began his solo.

Tap Tap Tap Tap Tap Tap – CRASH!

One giant green leaf fell on top of the raindrops, knocking them over.

The raindrops collided with the tomatoes.

The tomatoes smashed into the string beans.

The string beans bumped into the bananas.

Perfect Peter turned his head to see what was happening and danced off the stage into the front row.

Miss Tutu fainted.

by Francesca Simon

Molly Moon's Incredible Book of Hypnotism

The room was quiet. Everyone sat wide-eyed and thunder-struck. Molly looked around, satisfied, and very impressed with herself that she hadn't needed to use her voice at all.

"In a minute I will sit down. When I do, I will clap my hands. When you hear me clap, you will all snap out of your trances and you won't remember that I hypnotized you at all... And from now on, whenever you remember nasty things you have said or done to Molly Moon, you will hit yourselves over the head with whatever you are carrying."

Molly left the stage and sat down. She clapped sharply once. She hadn't hypnotized everyone to love her. She didn't need to do that now. She just wanted to be sure she could manage a crowd, and she could. As the room came to life around her, Molly reached into her pocket, pulled out the sheet of paper that she'd found in Adderstone's files and ripped it up.

So far in life, Molly had drawn a short straw. Now she was going to get what was due to her. A life like the world of Molly's favourite adverts. It might be just around the corner. Molly shivered with anticipation as she thought of all the lovely things she'd always wanted but never had. She'd line her pockets with the talent competition prize money, but that would just be for starters. She felt sure that with hypnotism under her belt, she'd never be short of money again.

by Georgia Byng

The Owl who was Afraid of the Dark

Plop opened his eyes and peered down through the leaves. There were people running about in his field, and flames were flickering from a pile of sticks. Another bonfire! Did that mean more fireworks?

Plop watched excitedly. He could see now that the people running about were boys – quite big boys in shorts. They were collecting more wood for the fire.

Suddenly they all disappeared into the woods with squeals and yells. All but one, that is – there was one boy left, sitting on a log near the fire.

Plop forgot about being afraid of the dark. He had to know what was going on. So he shut his eyes, took a deep breath, and fell off his branch.

The ground was nearer than he expected it to be, and he landed with an enormous thud.

"Coo!" said the boy on the log. "A roly-poly pudding! Who threw that?"

"Nobody threw me – I just came," said the roly-poly pudding, "and actually I'm a barn owl."

"So you are," said the boy. "Have you fallen out of your nest?"

Plop drew himself up as tall as he could.

"I did not fall – I flew," he said. "I'm just not a very good lander, that's all."

by Jill Tomlinson

Shadow of the Minotaur

It was dark in the palace of King Minos and it took Phoenix a few moments to get accustomed to the gloom.

"You there, Dad?" he whispered.

"Right behind you."

They were edging cautiously down a flight of stone stairs.

"I thought we were starting at the labyrinth," Phoenix hissed.

"We are. These are the steps leading down to the entrance. I should know. I helped design them."

"And that light?"

Phoenix was pointing at a faint glimmer below them.

"Princess Ariadne," said Dad. "She's waiting with the ball of thread and the sword."

"That's OK," Phoenix told him impatiently. "You don't need to tell me everything. I only wanted to know *where* I was. I know the legend better than you, remember."

It was brighter at the bottom of the stairs. Torches stood in iron brackets, flaring with every whisper of breeze. In their flickering light he saw the dark-eyed girl who had watched him break and run. It was hard to believe she was no more than a graphic projection.

"Prince Theseus," said Ariadne, approaching him. "I was only able to slip away for a few minutes. My father is suspicious. Here." She handed him the thread and sword. He felt the usual vibration against his wrist as his score built up. "Take these. The thread will lead you back to the entrance. The sword −"

"Yes," said Phoenix. "I think I know what to do with the sword."

by Alan Gibbons

The Snow Spider Trilogy

Gwyn returned minutes later and, having quietly divested himself of snow-soaked garments, crept barefoot up to the bedroom.

"It's done!" he told Eirlys. "The spell's begun!"

"Your friend was here!" she said.

"Alun? What did he want?"

"To see you! He was angry!"

"Where has he gone?" Gwyn began to feel a terrible apprehension overwhelming him.

"I think he went on to the mountain," Eirlys replied with equal consternation.

"I didn't see him. He must have missed the track!"

"He'll get lost!"

"Trapped!" cried Gwyn. "Trapped and frozen!" He tore down the stairs and out into the snow, forgetting, in his panic, to put on his boots, or his mac, or to shut the front door. He called his friend's name, again and again as he ran, until he was hoarse. The snow had become a fog, still and heavy, like a blanket, smothering any sound.

He found his way, with difficulty, to the place where he had touched the pillar of ice. There was another beside it now, and another and another; they rose higher than he could reach and too close to pass through. A wall of ice! Gwyn beat upon the wall, he kicked it, tore at it with his fingers, all the while calling Alun's name in his feeble croaking voice, and then he slid to the ground, defeated by his own spell.

by Jenny Nimmo

Alice in Wonderland

The Caterpillar and Alice looked at each other for some time in silence: at last the Caterpillar took the hookah out of its mouth, and addressed her in a languid, sleepy voice.

"Who are *you*?" said the Caterpillar.

This was not an encouraging opening for a conversation. Alice replied, rather shyly, "I – I hardly know, sir, just at present – at least I know who I *was* when I got up this morning, but I think I must have been changed several times since then."

"What do you mean by that?" said the Caterpillar sternly. "Explain yourself!"

"I can't explain *myself*, I'm afraid, sir," said Alice, "because I'm not myself, you see."

"I don't see," said the Caterpillar.

"I'm afraid I can't put it more clearly," Alice replied very politely, "for I can't understand it myself to being with; and being so many different sizes in a day is very confusing."

"It isn't," said the Caterpillar.

"Well, perhaps you haven't found it so yet," said Alice; "but when you have to turn into a chrysalis – you will some day, you know – and then after that into a butterfly, I should think you'll feel it a little queer, won't you?"

"Not a bit," said the Caterpillar.

"Well, perhaps your feelings may be different," said Alice; "all I know is, it would feel very queer to *me*."

"You!" said the Caterpillar contemptuously. "Who are *you*?"

by Lewis Carroll

GRADE THREE – VERSE

Testing

"Flies taste with their feet."
They said on T.V.

I thought I'd give it a try
And walked barefoot
On the early morning lawn.

I was surprised to find
That I could make distinctions
Even with my eyes shut.

Green blades on young grass
Were juicy like coarse chopped spinach
And thistle points were hot pin-pricks
Of grains of pepper.

Buttercups were a disappointment
So many shiny sweet wrappings,
All colour and no flavour.
And daisies kept their heads down
Not giving much away

But I really enjoyed the moss.
Full of nice chewy but gentle scrunchiness.

Dad said my brain needed testing,
So I stood on my head.
But that didn't work.

by Bob Sparrow

The Dentist and the Crocodile

The crocodile, with cunning smile, sat in the dentist's chair.
He said, "Right here and everywhere my teeth require repair."
The dentist's face was turning white. He quivered, quaked
    and shook.
He muttered, "I suppose I'm going to have to take a look."
"I want you", Crocodile declared, "to do the back ones first.
The molars at the very back are easily the worst."
He opened wide his massive jaws. It was a fearsome sight –
At least three hundred pointed teeth, all sharp and shining
    white.
The dentist kept himself well clear. He stood two yards away.
He chose the longest probe he had to search out the decay.
"I said to do the *back ones* first!" the Crocodile called out.
"You're much too far away, dear sir, to see what you're about.
To do the back ones properly you've got to put your head
Deep down inside my great big mouth," the grinning Crocky
    said.
The poor old dentist wrung his hands and, weeping in despair,
He cried, "No no! I see them all extremely well from here!"
Just then, in burst a lady, in her hands a golden chain.
She cried, "Oh Croc, you naughty boy, you're playing tricks
    again!"
"Watch out!" the dentist shrieked and started climbing up the
    wall.
"He's after me! He's after you! He's going to eat us all!"
"Don't be a twit," the lady said, and flashed a gorgeous smile.
"He's harmless. He's my little pet, my lovely crocodile."

by Roald Dahl

Christmas Thank Yous

Dear Auntie
Oh, what a nice jumper
I've always adored powder blue
and fancy you thinking of
orange and pink
for the stripes
how clever of you

Dear Uncle
The soap is
terrific
So
useful
and such a kind thought and
how did you guess that
I'd just used the last of
the soap that last Christmas brought

Dear Gran
Many thanks for the hankies
Now I really can't wait for the flu
and the daisies embroidered
in red round the 'M'
for Michael
how
thoughtful of you

Dear Cousin
What socks!
and the same sort you wear
so you must be
the last word in style
and I'm certain you're right that the
luminous green
will make me stand out a mile

Dear Sister
I quite understand your concern
it's a risk sending jam in the post
But I think I've pulled out
all the big bits
of glass
so it won't taste too sharp
spread on toast.

Dear Grandad
Don't fret
I'm delighted
So *don't* think your gift will
offend
I'm not at all hurt
that you gave up this year
and just sent me
a fiver
to spend

by Mick Gowar

The Hurt Boy and the Birds

The hurt boy talked to the birds
and fed them the crumbs of his heart.

It was not easy to find the words
for secrets he hid under his skin.
The hurt boy spoke of a bully's fist
that made his face a bruised moon –
his spectacles stamped to ruin.

It was not easy to find the words
for things that nightly hissed
as if his pillow was a hideaway for creepy-crawlies –
the note sent to the girl he fancied

held high in mockery.
But the hurt boy talked to the birds
and their feathers gave him welcome –

Their wings taught him new ways to become.

by John Agard

Snow

No breath of wind,
No gleam of sun –
Still the white snow
Whirls softly down –
Twig and bough
And blade and thorn
All in an icy
Quiet, forlorn.
Whispering, rustling,
Through the air,
On sill and stone,
Roof – everywhere,
It heaps its powdery
Crystal flakes,
Of every tree
A mountain makes;
Till pale and faint
At shut of day,
Stoops from the West
One wintry ray.
And, feathered in fire,
Where ghosts the moon,
A robin shrills
His lonely tune.

by Walter de la Mare

Babies are Boring

Babies are boring
(Oh yes they are!)
Don't believe mothers
or a doting papa.
Babies are boring
their hands and their bellies,
their pink puffy faces
which wobble like jellies.
Accountants and grandmas
and sailors from Chile
when faced with a baby
act extraordinarily silly.
They grimace and they giggle,
say "diddle-dum-do",
they waggle their fingers
(stick their tongues out too).
They slaver and slurp
then they tickle its tummy,
they gurgle and drool:
"Oh, he's just like his mummy!"
"Oh, his mouth is like Herbert's!"
"He's got Uncle Fred's nose!"
"My word, he looks healthy!"
"It's his feed, I suppose?"
Save me from baldness
and the old smell of kippers,
but most of all save me
from all gooey nippers.
I'm a brute, I'm a fiend
and no use to implore me
to tickle its chin,
because all babies bore me.

by Peter Mortimer

Dreaming the Unicorn

I dreamed I saw the Unicorn
last night.
It rippled through the forest,
pearly white,
breathing a moonlit silence.

Its single horn
stood shining like a lance.
I saw it toss its head
and snort and prance
and paw the midnight air.
Its mane was like a mass
of silver hair.

My mind was wild, unclear.
I could not think or speak.
Above my head, I heard the branches creak
and then, from where I stood,
I watched it flicker off into the wood,
into the velvet space between the trees.

A sudden rush of rapid midnight breeze,
that felt both chill and deep,
awoke me from my sleep,
and there upon the pillow by my head
I found a strand of shining silver thread.

I kept that strand of mane,
I kept it, still,
inside a box upon my window sill.
And when the world hangs heavy
on my brain,
it helps me dream the Unicorn again.

by Tony Mitton

Tracey's Tree

Last year it was not there,
the sapling with purple leaves
planted in the school grounds with care.
It's Tracey's tree, my friend who died,
and last year it was not there.

Tracey the girl with long black hair,
who, out playing one day, ran
across a main road for a dare.
The lorry struck her. Now a tree grows
and last year it was not there.

Through the classroom window I stare
and watch the sapling sway.
Soon its branches will stand bare.
It wears a forlorn and lonely look
and last year it was not there.

October's chill is in the air
and cold rain distorts my view.
I feel a sadness that's hard to bear.
The tree blurs, as if I've been crying,
and last year it was not there.

by Wes Magee

GRADE THREE – PROSE

Artemis Fowl

Mulch withdrew his thumbs and, after a quick wipe, thrust them in his mouth, allowing the natural balm in his saliva to begin the healing process. Of course if he'd still had his magic, he could have just wished the scorched digits better. But that was the price you paid for a life of crime.

Wart-face didn't look so good. Smoke was leaking from every orifice in his head. Flameproof goblins may be, but the errant fireball had given his tubes a good scouring. He swayed like a strand of seaweed, then collapsed face down on the concrete floor. Something crunched. Probably a big goblin nose.

The other gang members did not react favourably.

"Look what he did to the boss!"

"That stinkin' stump."

"Let's fry 'im."

Mulch backed up even further. He'd been hoping the remaining goblins would lose their nerve once their leader was out of commission. Apparently not. Even though it was most definitely not in his nature, Mulch had no option but to attack.

He unhinged his jaw and leaped forward, clamping his teeth around the foremost goblin's head.

"Ow, bagg off!" he shouted around the obstruction in his mouth. "Bagg off or ur briend gedds it!"

The others froze, uncertain of their next move. Of course they'd all seen what dwarf molars could do to a goblin head. Not a pretty sight.

by Eoin Colfer

What Katy Did

It was a big place, with a very high roof. There was not much wood left in it just now, and the little there was, was piled neatly about the sides of the shed, so as to leave plenty of room. The place felt cool and dark, and the motion of the swing seemed to set the breeze blowing. It waved Katy's hair like a great fan, and made her dreamy and quiet. All sorts of sleepy ideas began to flit through her brain. Swinging to and fro like the pendulum of a great clock, she gradually rose higher and higher, driving herself along by the motion of her body, and striking the floor smartly with her foot at every sweep. Now she was at the top of the high-arched door. Then she could almost touch the crossbeam above it, and through the small square window could see pigeons sitting and pluming themselves on the eaves of the barn and white clouds blowing over the blue sky. She had never swung so high before. It was like flying she thought, as she bent and curved more strongly in the seat, trying to send herself yet higher and graze the roof with her toes.

Suddenly at the very highest point of the sweep there was a sharp noise of cracking. The swing gave a violent twist, spun half round and tossed Katy into the air. She clutched the rope – felt it dragged from her grasp – then down – down – she fell. All grew dark, and she knew no more.

by Susan Coolidge

Smugglers

"Move yourself then, nipper!"

Grampy already had the end of Reuben's cliff rope fastened round his own waist. He thrust the rest of the coil at Reuben then sat down heavily.

"Hurry, or the land crabs'll take the lot!"

Reuben dashed into the sea, knotting the other end of the rope round him as he went. The line, with Grampy as anchor, gave him an advantage. He might be knocked over by the breaking surf but didn't fear being washed away. All around him, squeals of excitement were changing to sudden frightened shouts as fellow plunderers were dragged from their feet by the undertow and reduced to clawing their way back to shore on all fours, like survivors of the wreck itself.

Survivors. Were there any? She was a good-sized ship: three masts, two of them broken as she'd rolled in the surf before coming to rest. She must have a crew of more than twenty, and none were to be seen.

Reuben was swallowed by a towering wave, and as he clung to his rope amid the swirling roar of water, something banged into him. The wave surged on up the beach and as Reuben staggered, choking, to his feet again, he saw through stinging eyes that he'd been hit by a body. It lay lifeless on its back beside him, its mouth and eyes gaping. Then the spent wave retreated, dragging at the lifeless body as it went, sucking it back into the deep.

"Grab him!" roared Grampy from the beach, the rope taut in his hands.

And Reuben dug his heels into the sliding shingle and clung to the corpse.

by Christopher Russell

The Blue Roan Child

Be quiet, she told herself. *He'll hear you breathing.*

The captain descended the steps and paused at the gateway that led into the southwest quad. Looking down the weapons yard, he gave somebody a nod, then opened the gate just enough to get out. A yard worker arrived to close it behind him. The worker paused to give the pit fire a rake – Syeira could hear the hissing of coals – and returned to the other end of the yard.

Then came the clang of the keep door. *Finally*. The colts were coming out.

She crouched down even farther. She could only hope the colts wouldn't smell her and betray her presence. The fire in the pit was burning well; like all wild things they hated fire, and would stay away from this end of the yard. That was the idea, anyway. Now she could sense their unruly presence, hear their neighs, feel the vibrations of their hooves under her feet. She knew that Davy would have torches and lassos ready, in case they turned on him...

The thought of torches spurred her on.

This is it.

She put a hand to the spice pouch under her jerkin. The devil's scratch was with Grulla, but in its place she had put the hank of Arwin's mane, the original one that Grulla had cut off. She couldn't have taken on a job like this without a charm. She took a deep breath.

Now.

by Jamieson Findlay

Hitler's Canary

"Stick 'em up, pardner," he kept saying in a fake American accent while he used his fingers as a gun. We were in Anton's flat pretending to shoot each other when I managed to corner him on the small balcony outside the living room.

"Now you can't escape!" I cried, holding both hands out as six shooters.

Anton grinned at me. "Oh yes I can, pardner. What you don't know is that I have my trusty horse below this balcony. I shall leap upon him and ride to freedom."

With those words Anton suddenly jumped from the balcony. My heart stopped. I felt sure he was going to kill himself – I couldn't think what I would tell his mother but I knew she would be cross. I looked over the edge of the balcony just in time to see Anton land smack bang on the back of Mrs Jensen's cow. He landed rather well and managed to grab the rope around the poor cow's neck and pretend to ride off. I think he might have got away with it if he hadn't decided to yell "Yee ha!" at the same time. Bess was so startled that she banged backwards into Mama's roses, got a great thorn in her backside and surged forwards into the holly bush. At this point Anton lost his grip and slid sideways into the ornamental fish pond. He came out soaking wet and we both laughed so much we couldn't speak.

by Sandi Toksvig

The Demon Headmaster

Dinah found herself shivering. Ridiculously, she expected him to have pink eyes, because the rest of his face was so colourless. Or perhaps no eyes at all...

But his eyes were not pink. They were large and luminous, and a peculiar sea-green colour. She had never seen eyes like them before, and she found herself staring into them. Staring and staring.

"Funny you should be so tired," he said, softly. "So early in the morning."

She opened her mouth to say that she was not tired, but, to her surprise, she yawned instead.

"So tired," crooned the Headmaster, his huge, extraordinary eyes fixed on her face. "You can hardly move your arms and legs. You are so tired, so tired. You feel your head begin to nod and slowly, slowly your eyes are starting to close. *So* tired and sleepy."

He's mad, Dinah thought muzzily. *The whole school's raving mad.* But she felt her eyes start to close, in spite of all she could do. She was drifting, drifting... All she could see was two pools, deep green like the sea, and she seemed to sink into them as she drifted off and off...

She opened her eyes again and gave a nervous laugh. "I'm sorry. What did you say?"

"You fell asleep," the Headmaster said coldly. "You have been asleep for a long time." He put his glasses on again.

"Asleep?" Dinah stared.

"For the whole morning."

by Gillian Cross

Here Lies Arthur

"They're coming." He's breathless. "Their scouts came at dawn. They saw our men at the ford and heard their challenges, and laughed when they saw how few there were. Now the whole band is moving up, wagons and everything..."

Through the trees behind him we catch distant shouts. Insults are bellowing back and forth across the ford. We strain our ears. We cup our hands around them to catch the drips of sound. We can't make out words, and even if we could, the Saxons speak a different tongue from ours. But we all hear the shouting blur into a roar as the attackers surge forward into the ford. It's that battle-noise again, that ugly music woven out of shouting voices and hoof-falls and the clang of swords. I start to wish I'd stayed with my master. Then we hear the high horns ringing, calling Arthur's hidden riders out of the woods.

"Mount up!" shouts Medrawt, who Arthur's put in charge of us. He feels ashamed at being left to lead this rag-tag army of boys, and he cuffs the heads of those who stand closest and bellows loud to make himself feel better. "Ride!"

by Philip Reeve

The Hundred-Mile-an-Hour Dog

"Walkies!" I cried and dropped Streaker on to the whirring track.

There was a startled yelp as Streaker was caught by the carpet and hurled backwards at high speed. She shot off the rear of the track, whizzed out through the door, rocketed across the kitchen, and ended up with her backside rammed in the open front of the washing-machine – which luckily wasn't switched on.

Streaker fixed me with a bewildered gaze as if to say, "How on earth did I get into *this* position?" Her front paws were firmly on the ground, but the back half of her was even more firmly wedged in the washing-machine. I ran over and tried to pull her out as gently as I could, but Streaker was jammed there like King Arthur's sword in the stone.

"Now what?" Tina gave me a silent shrug.

"She can't move," I went on. "We've got to get her out. We need help."

Tina shrugged again. "What kind of help?" she said. "Who do we ask? Plumbers? A garage? Fire brigade?"

"Fire brigade!" I leaped to the telephone. "They get cats out of trees and things, don't they? Maybe they get dogs out of washing-machines."

by Jeremy Strong

GRADE FOUR – VERSE

Assembly

Somebody whispered something
and a little titter
skittered and scuttled along the rows
then burrowed under a heap of teachers' frowns.
Nobody spoke.
The hall was huge with silence.
No words fluttered on the empty air,
only dust motes moved
in the curious light
that chinned itself up to the window
and peered through.
Somebody coughed.
Feet shuffled themselves.
The headmaster banged his fist
until the startled lectern jumped with fright.

"You! You down there!
That boy in the green shirt!"
His signpost finger zapped us all,
but nobody moved;
nobody spoke.
Only the titter, feral as anything,
blundered around the room,
seeking escape.

Well, I mean, the school uniform –
it's grey trousers –
and the shirt is green.

by Anne Bell

Creative Writing

My story on Monday began:
Mountainous seas crashed on the cliffs,
And the desolate land grew wetter...
The teacher wrote a little note: *Remember the capital letter!*

My poem on Tuesday began:
Red tongues of fire,
Licked higher and higher
From smoking Etna's top...
The teacher wrote a little note: *Where is your full stop?*

My story on Wednesday began:
Through the lonely, pine-scented wood
There twists a hidden path...
The teacher wrote a little note: *Start a paragraph!*

My poem on Thursday began:
The trembling child,
Eyes dark and wild,
Frozen midst the fighting...
The teacher wrote a little note: *Take care – untidy writing!*

My story on Friday began:
The boxer bruised and bloody lay,
His eye half closed and swollen...
The teacher wrote a little note: *Use a semi-colon!*

Next Monday my story will begin:
Once upon a time...

by Gervase Phinn

Spotlight

Switch the spotlights on.
Make them mainly white
but have at least one red or blue.
Turn one light on each of you,
and when you're lit,
break out, have some fun –
dance, one-legged, till you sweat,
shake, collapsing in a pool,
sing a quaky, wordless song,
pretend to be a vulture,
act the ancient high-bred fool,
lie down, clap your feet,
mime a waking panther,
or a dog that's just been stung –
or any act that takes your fancy
in that round of light.
Don't stand back and crush the wall.
Don't put up a fight.
We need some wild applause,
but first we need SPOTLIGHT!

by Matthew Sweeney

The Elephant Child

Under an African sun he stands,
the elephant child,
hot and hungry and thirsty.
He's as big as a car
but still small for an elephant.
Sadly swinging his trunk he stands
for many hours beside his mother,
trying to coax and nudge her back to life
to take him home.
He could not help her when the men came.
They just laughed at him.
And now
under an African moon he stands
and tries to make sense of her butchered face.
Then he cries as only an elephant can cry
but he does not understand.
Neither do I.

by Sue Cowling

GRADE FOUR – PROSE

Raven's Gate

There was a car parked between the fire and the fence – Matt thought it might be a Saab or a Jaguar. A man got out but he was silhouetted against the light and Matt couldn't make out who he was. The man raised a hand and the gold signet ring he was wearing momentarily flashed red, reflecting the light of the fire.

He had given a signal. A lorry that was parked on the other side of the clearing immediately began to reverse right up to the corridor that joined the giant sphere of Omega One to the rest of the building. As Matt watched, the doors of the lorry were thrown open and several men emerged, dressed in strange, cumbersome clothes. They congregated together, then lifted something: a large silver box about five metres long. It was obviously heavy. They took a lot of time lowering it to the ground.

Matt couldn't quite see what was going on. He had to get closer. He followed the fence back to the gap he'd discovered the last time he was here and waited, making sure nobody was looking in his direction. But all the villagers were concentrating on the lorry. Matt chose his moment, then dived forward, head first. He felt the jagged edge of the wire tear his shirt and scrape his back, but he was lucky. He hadn't drawn blood. He landed face down on the grass and lay still.

by Anthony Horowitz

Shadowmancer

Beadle grasped his companion's cloak even tighter as a gentle breeze rustled the brown, crisp leaves in the trees.

"Is it a man or is it...them?" He could hardly say the words; his right leg shook, his eyelids twitched, his mouth went dry and his tongue stuck to the roof of his mouth.

"Them?" hissed his companion in his face. "Who are *them*? Can't you say the word? What are you frightened of?"

Beadle hunched his shoulders and buried his face in the musty black cloak of his tall, angry companion. "Thulak," he whispered feebly, trying to muffle his voice so they would not hear him.

His companion raised both his hands and cupped his mouth like the bell of a trumpet; he took in a deep breath and with a voice that came from the depths of his soul, he bellowed: "Thulak. Thulak. Thulak." The voice echoed around the woods, the fox scurried from the brush and ran deeper into the undergrowth.

A roost of the blackest rooks lifted from the trees above their heads and their *caw-caw-caw* filled the night sky as they circled above the branches, dancing in the moonlight.

"... *No*," whispered the now terrified Beadle. "Please, Parson Demurral, don't say that word, they will hear and they will come and get us, my mother said..."

He was hastily interrupted.

"*Us*, Beadle? Did you say *us*?" Demurral towered over the cowering, frightened form of his servant. "I fear nothing and no one, and they have every reason in the world to fear me.

by G P Taylor

The Giver

"You're hit, Jonas!" Asher yelled from behind the tree. "Pow! You're hit again!"

Jonas stood alone in the centre of the field. Several of the children raised their heads and looked at him uneasily. The attacking armies slowed, emerged from their crouched positions, and watched to see what he was doing.

In his mind, Jonas saw again the face of the boy who had lain dying on a field and had begged him for water. He had a sudden choking feeling, as if it were difficult to breathe.

One of the children raised an imaginary rifle and made an attempt to destroy him with a firing noise. "Pssheeew!" Then they were all silent, standing awkwardly, and the only sound was the sound of Jonas's shuddering breaths. He was struggling not to cry.

Gradually, when nothing happened, nothing changed, the children looked at each other nervously and went away. He heard the sounds as they righted their bicycles and began to ride down the path that led from the field.

Only Asher and Fiona remained.

"What's wrong, Jonas? It was only a game," Fiona said.

"You ruined it," Asher said in an irritated voice.

"Don't play it any more," Jonas pleaded.

by Lois Lowry

The Wee Free Men

It was dark inside the tent, as well as stuffy and hot. A skinny figure sat behind a small table. She had a very sharp, thin nose and was wearing a large black straw hat with paper flowers on it. It was completely unsuitable for a face like that.

"Are you a witch?" said Tiffany. "I don't mind if you are."

"What a strange question to spring on someone," said the woman, looking slightly shocked. "Your baron bans witches in this country, you know that, and the first thing you say to me is 'Are you a witch?' Why would I be a witch?"

"Well, you're wearing all black," said Tiffany.

"Anyone can wear black," said the woman. "That doesn't mean a thing."

"And you're wearing a straw hat with flowers in it," Tiffany went on.

"Aha!" said the woman. "That proves it, then. Witches wear tall pointy hats. Everyone knows that, foolish child."

"Yes, but witches are also very clever," said Tiffany calmly. There was something about the twinkle in the woman's eyes that told her to carry on. "They sneak about. Probably they often don't look like witches. And a witch coming here would know about the Baron and so she'd wear the kind of hat that everyone knows witches don't wear."

The woman stared at her. "That was an incredible feat of reasoning," she said at last. "You'd make a good witch-finder. You know they used to set fire to witches? Whatever kind of hat I've got on, you'd say it proves I'm a witch, yes?"

"Well, the frog sitting on your hat is a bit of a clue, too," said Tiffany.

"I'm a toad, actually," said the creature.

by Terry Pratchett

Chinese Cinderella

"Who are these little hooligans," Niang began, her voice seething with anger, "making such a racket in the living-room downstairs?"

"They're my friends from school."

"Who invited them here?"

"No one."

"What are they doing here?"

"They came to celebrate my winning the election for class president."

"Is this party your idea?"

"No, Niang." I shook my head in denial. "They came of their own accord. I didn't know anything about it."

"Come here!" she screamed. I approached her gingerly, trembling with terror. She slapped my face so hard I almost fell. "Liar! You planned it, didn't you, to show off our house to your penniless classmates. How dare you!"

"No, I didn't." Tears streaked down my cheeks and I found it hard to breathe.

"Your father works so hard to feed and clothe all of you. He comes home for a nap and there's not a moment of peace. What insolence to invite them into our living-room and make such a racket!"

"I never asked them here. They know I'm not allowed to go to their house after school so they decided to visit me instead."

She slapped me with the back of her hand against my other cheek. "Show-off! I'll teach you to be so sneaky!" she screamed loudly. "Go downstairs this minute and tell your hooligan friends to get out! They are not welcome!"

by Adeline Yen Mah

Out of the Ashes

We were having supper when the phone rang. Auntie Liz answered it. I knew right away something was wrong, and I knew from the moment she looked at me exactly what it was. She handed me the phone. Mum was trying not to cry as she told me. She hadn't wanted to worry me about it yesterday, she said, but the vet had been called in yesterday morning. Dad had found blisters on the feet of one of our sows, Jessica, and was worried about a couple of sheep that were limping badly. Tests had confirmed it. We had foot and mouth disease on the farm. There was an 'A' notice on the farm gate which meant no one was allowed in or out except the vets and the slaughterers. The animals would be put down tomorrow. So I'd have to stay with Auntie Liz until it was all over. It would be the best place for me, she said.

When I asked how Dad was, she said he was very calm, as if he'd been expecting it all along. She said she'd phone again tomorrow, and that she loved me. I don't remember the last time she said that to me. She sounded almost like a different person.

I've been sitting here on the bed in a daze ever since. Not crying. I can't cry. It's me who's done this, it must be. I brought the infection back with me from Mr Bailey's farm. Ruby or Bobs or me, but whichever of us it was, it had been my doing, my fault. I had sentenced our animals to death.

by Michael Morpurgo

The Diamond of Drury Lane

Pedro gave me a deep bow, accepting the challenge. I was about to run off but he gestured to me to sit on the anchor that dressed the stage. I was surprised: I had thought that Pedro Hawkins was only interested in having the stage to himself. As it would have looked strange if I had refused, I sat down. All these years of living in the theatre, I'd never been on the boards with a full audience in front of me. I felt heady with excitement.

Pedro composed himself to play. Signor Angelini raised his baton and signalled for his protégé to start. Pedro then began the most extraordinary dance I had ever seen. With legs stamping like in an Irish jig, upper body still, he began to play a hornpipe. Sitting so close to him, I could see the beads of sweat flying from his brow, but all the time he kept an impassive expression on his face. From a distance, it would look as if he was having to make no effort. The audience began to clap in time to the music. He went faster and faster. I thought that it must be impossible for him to carry on playing without losing step or fluffing a note, but no. It was almost as if he had found freedom in the dance and would take flight if it did not end soon. I could see him do it: he'd fly out of the theatre, out of the smoke of London, into the blue sky and home to his land of hot sun and friendly faces. But before his wings had a chance to sprout, he brought the hornpipe to an end with a flourish.

The applause was immense.

by Julia Golding

Wolf Brother

In the Forest, a twig snapped.

Torak spun round.

The darkness was absolute. Everywhere he looked the shadows were bear-shaped.

No wind.

No birdsong.

Just the crackle of the fire and the thud of his heart. The Forest itself was holding its breath.

His father licked the sweat from his lips. "It's not here yet," he said. "Soon. It will come for me soon... Quick. The knives."

Torak didn't want to swap knives. That would make it final. But his father was watching him with an intensity that allowed no refusal.

Clenching his jaw so hard that it hurt, Torak took his own knife and put it into Fa's hand. Then he untied the buckskin sheath from his father's belt. Fa's knife was beautiful and deadly, with a blade of banded blue slate shaped like a willow leaf, and a haft of red deer antler that was bound with elk sinew for a better grip. As Torak looked down at it, the truth hit him. He was getting ready for a life without Fa. "I'm not leaving you!" he cried. "I'll fight it, I –"

"No! No-one can fight this bear!"

Ravens flew up from the trees.

Torak forgot to breathe.

by Michelle Paver

GRADE FIVE – VERSE

Water Picture

In the pond in the park
all things are doubled:
Long buildings hang and
wriggle gently. Chimneys
are bent legs bouncing
on clouds below. A flag
wags like a fish-hook
down there in the sky.

The arched stone bridge
is an eye, with underlid
in the water. In its lens
dip crinkled heads with hats
that don't fall off. Dogs go by,
barking on their backs...

Treetops deploy a haze of
cherry bloom for roots,
where birds coast belly-up
in the glass bowl of a hill...

A swan, with twin necks
forming the figure three,
steers between two dimpled
towers doubled. Fondly,
hissing, she kisses herself,
and all the scene is troubled:
water-windows splinter,
tree-limbs tangle, the bridge
folds like a fan.

by May Swenson

Someone Let the Cat Out

Someone let the cat out
And the cat
Spat
Whiskered through the night
Streaking like a comet
Through the low lamp light

Someone let the cat out
And the beast
Greased
Lightning in the sky
Flashed between the houses
And shook them with his cry

Someone let the cat out
And the world
Hurled
Curses at his head
As they heard the cry and woke
And staggered out of bed

Someone let the cat out
And the cry
Died
Sudden in the air
A skid a screech a crash
And then a silence everywhere

Someone let the cat out
And a man
Ran
Owing life to luck
And the people came and shuddered
For the cat had squashed a truck

by Jonathan C Lamb

Mirage

On this, the hottest of summer days,
A lake appears in the shimmering haze,
A haunting lake on the desert sand,
A taunting call to the weary band
Who've traipsed for hours in the blazing heat,
And rejoice to see the lustrous sheet
Of water on the horizon bare.
But elation turns to bleak despair
As the ephemeral lake is quickly gone,
And another appears much further on.

When the midday sun the saltbush sears,
In the burnished distance there appears
A concrete city, tall and wide,
In this uninhabited countryside.
The buildings reach for the open sky
And the outback traveller can't deny
What his own eyes see on the gibber plain.
Then the city fades, and he seeks in vain
To find the non-existent town
Whose spectral walls have tumbled down.

As the warmth disturbs the outback air,
I see great castles standing there.
And then appears across the sky
A herd of camels flying by.
The camels leave, and a kangaroo
Hops lazily 'cross the distant blue;
And twisted trees materialize
In the heavens before my very eyes!
Mirages daily haunt the track
Of those who travel the great Outback!

by Philip R Rush

Black Monday Lovesong

In love's dances, in love's dances,
One retreats and one advances.
One grows warmer and one colder,
One more hesitant, one bolder.
One gives what the other needed
Once, or will need, now unheeded.
One is clenched, compact, ingrowing
While the other's melting, flowing.
One is smiling and concealing
While the other's asking, kneeling.
One is arguing or sleeping
While the other's weeping, weeping.

And the question finds no answer
And the tune misleads the dancer
And the lost look finds no other
And the lost hand finds no brother
And the word is left unspoken
Till the theme and thread are broken.

When shall these divisions alter?
Echo's answer seems to falter:
'Oh the unperplexed, unvexed time
Next time... one day... one day... next time!'

by A S J Tessimond

Full Moon and Little Frieda

A cool small evening shrunk to a dog bark and the clank of a
    bucket –

And you listening.
A spider's web, tense for the dew's touch.
A pail lifted, still and brimming – mirror
To tempt a first star to a tremor.

Cows are going home in the lane there, looping the hedges
    with their warm wreaths of breath –
A dark river of blood, many boulders,
Balancing unspilled milk.

"Moon!" you cry suddenly, "Moon! Moon!"

The moon has stepped back like an artist gazing amazed at a
    work

That points at him amazed.

by Ted Hughes

The Witch

I have walked a great while over the snow,
And I am not tall nor strong.
My clothes are wet, and my teeth are set,
And the way was hard and long.
I have wandered over the fruitful earth,
But I never came here before.
Oh, lift me over the threshold, and let me in at the door!

The cutting wind is a cruel foe.
I dare not stand in the blast.
My hands are stone, and my voice a groan,
And the worst of death is past.
I am but a little maiden still,
My little white feet are sore.
Oh, lift me over the threshold, and let me in at the door!

Her voice was the voice that women have,
Who plead for their heart's desire.
She came—she came—and the quivering flame
Sunk and died in the fire.
It never was lit again on my hearth
Since I hurried across the floor,
To lift her over the threshold, and let her in at the door.

by Mary Elizabeth Coleridge

The Tunnel

This is the way that I have to go
I've left all my friends behind
Back there, where a faint light glimmers
Round the long tunnel's bend.

I can't see a roof up above me,
I can't find either wall,
My shoes slip on the slimy boulders –
How far is it down, if I fall?

Beneath me the same stream is flowing
That laughed in the fields back there –
Here, it is black, like the leeches and weeds,
And the bats flitting through the dank air.

It's just the same if I shut my eyes:
My companions, all around,
Are trickles, drips, sploshes, sudden *plops*,
Then, a strange, sucking sound.

One shoe's full of the cold dark water,
My hands slither over the stones,
My throat's gone dry, my heart pound-pounds,
But I can only go on –

Till I can see them, they can see me
And again they start to shout,
The rats bite, watch out for the rats,
But now I am almost out:

Dizzy, happy, I blink at the light,
The sun's still shining, the birds still sing.
Someone is patting me on the back –
Now I am one of the gang.

by Brian Lee

Remember

Remember wings when you think of spells,
Wings of the butterfly, wings of a swift,
Think of the sky and the loop and lift
Of the seagulls' wings and their swoop and drift.
 A spell is how a bird feels

When it takes to the cloud-puffed air
And feels the wind for the first time over its wings,
Feels their delicate flutterings.
Spells are this and other things,
 Often clasped in a rhyme.

When you think of spells remember the best
Dreams you had on a day of sun
When the colour of Poppy and Buttercup ran,
When the world of creatures first began
 And everything was blessed.

You cannot expect or search for a spell.
It comes to you with the rise of a breeze,
Runs through your veins as wind uses trees.
It is the voice of the changing seas
 Caught in the shape of a shell.

by Elizabeth Jennings

GRADE FIVE – PROSE

The No. 1 Ladies' Detective Agency

The man suddenly froze. "Don't make any sudden movement," he said very softly. "There it is. Look."

Mma Ramotswe peered into the engine space. For a few moments she could make out nothing unusual, but then the snake moved slightly and she saw it. She was right; it was a cobra, twined about the engine, its head moving slowly to right and left, as if seeking out something.

The man was quite still. Then he touched Mma Ramotswe on the forearm.

"Walk very carefully back to the door," he said. "Get into the cab, and start the engine. Understand?"

Mma Ramotswe nodded. Then, moving as slowly as she could, she eased herself into the driving seat and reached forward to turn the key.

The engine came into life immediately, as it always did. The tiny white van had never failed to start first time.

"Press the accelerator," yelled the man. "Race the engine!"

Mma Ramotswe did as she was told, and the engine roared throatily. There was a noise from the front, another thump, and then the man signalled to her to switch off. Mma Ramotswe did so, and waited to be told whether it was safe to get out.

"You can come out," he called. "That's the end of the cobra."

Mma Ramotswe got out of the cab and walked round to the front. Looking into the engine, she saw the cobra in two pieces, quite still.

"It had twined itself through the blades of the fan," said the man, making a face of disgust. "Nasty way to go, even for a snake. But it could have crept into the cab and bitten you, you know. So there we are. You are still alive."

by Alexander McCall Smith

War Horse

If it is possible to be happy in the middle of a nightmare, then Topthorn and I were happy that summer. Every day we had to make the same hazardous journeys up to the front line which in spite of almost continuous offensives and counter-offensives moved only a matter of a few hundred yards in either direction. Hauling our ambulance cart of dying and wounded back from the trenches we became a familiar sight along the pitted track. More than once we were cheered by marching soldiers as they passed us. Once, after we had plodded on, too tired to be fearful, through a devastating barrage that straddled the road in front of us and behind us, one of the soldiers with his tunic covered in blood and mud, came and stood by my head and threw his good arm around my neck and kissed me.

"Thank you, my friend," he said. "I never thought they would get us out of that hell-hole. I found this yesterday, and thought about keeping it for myself, but I know where it belongs." And he reached up and hung a muddied ribbon around my neck. There was an Iron Cross dangling on the end of it. "You'll have to share it with your friend," he said. "They tell me you're both English. I bet you are the first English in this war to win an Iron Cross, and the last I shouldn't wonder." The waiting wounded outside the hospital tent clapped and cheered us to the echo, bringing doctors, nurses and patients running out of the tent to see what there could be to clap about in the midst of all this misery.

by Michael Morpurgo

Daughter of Venice

A boy my size but a couple of years younger walks towards me. He's barefoot and in trousers, too, though he has a *bareta* on. I press against the wall to allow him passage. But he catches my eye, and his own glints. He also hugs the wall closer. I swerve out to go around him, but he quickly swerves himself and our shoulders bash hard.

"What you think you're doing here?" His face is mean. Three rings of dirt circle the creases of his neck. His breath smells of rancid figs. It warms my cheeks.

Warms my cheeks! No veil. I'm outside without a veil. That's what it means to be a boy – but, oh, it makes me feel as if I were naked. I fight the urge to cover my face with my hands.

"This spot's mine."

His language is crude and hard to follow. I have to get away from his nastiness fast. I lower my head and try again to pass.

He grabs me by the hair at the nape of my neck.

"What's this? What you doing with hair like this?"

I twist away, but he pins me to the wall.

"Whatever gimmick you've got, boy, go use it somewhere else." His face is so close to mine, I fear his lips will brush my cheek. "Don't ever let me see you begging around here again."

So that's it. "I'm not begging," I say reasonably. "I'm a fisherboy."

"With this white skin?" He pinches my cheek. "If you beg as bad as you lie, you'll not last long in this world. Take your fake fancy talk and go die somewhere else." He spits in my face and walks on.

I'm breathing heavily as I wipe the boy's saliva from my nose and brow. I want to go straight home. Now, this very instant. Straight into the arms of my clean, cooing sisters. But the beggar boy went in the direction of home. Oh, I spy him now, leaning against the wall by the opening of the alley that leads back to my *palazzo*. I have no choice; I hurry in the other direction, shaking with disgust.

by Donna Jo Napoli

I, Coriander

I tried to warn Gabriel not to open the door to the water gate, but everything was happening too fast. He pushed it open and beckoned us towards the steps. I could see no sign of the alligator, only the reflection of the moon on the river's surface. Hester and I scrambled into the boat and Gabriel grabbed the oars as I pushed us hard away from the steps and towards the water gate.

Too late. The raven was upon us, cawing loudly, swooping above our heads. Gabriel lifted an oar and hit out as hard as he could and we began to spin round and round. The raven flew up immediately above us, getting ready to attack. Then there was a swirl in the dark water and I saw a creamy white jaw with a mouthful of sharp pointed teeth take hold of the rope attached to our little boat.

"Sit down!" I shouted. It was just in time, for the boat took off as if we were being propelled by some wondrous machine. We all ducked low under the water gate out into the main flow of the river. The raven circled and flapped his wings but was soon left far behind.

Gabriel seized the oars. As he did so, our furious pace lessened and he soon had control of the boat. I saw the water heave and a dark shape slip back upstream.

"What in heaven's name has happened?" gasped Gabriel.

"I have no idea," I lied. "All that matters is that we have found Hester and she is alive and well."

by Sally Gardner

The Canterville Ghost

At eleven o'clock the family retired, and by half-past all the lights were out. Some time after, Mr Otis was awakened by a curious noise in the corridor, outside his room. It sounded like the clank of metal, and seemed to be coming nearer every moment. He got up at once, struck a match, and looked at the time. It was exactly one o'clock. He was quite calm, and felt his pulse, which was not at all feverish. The strange noise still continued, and with it he heard distinctly the sound of footsteps. He put on his slippers, took a small oblong phial out of his dressing-case, and opened the door. Right in front of him he saw, in the wan moonlight, an old man of terrible aspect. His eyes were as red burning coals; long grey hair fell over his shoulders in matted coils; his garments, which were of antique cut, were soiled and ragged and from his wrists and ankles hung heavy manacles and rusty gyves.

"My dear sir," said Mr Otis, "I really must insist on your oiling those chains, and have brought you for that purpose a small bottle of the Tammany Rising Sun Lubricator. It is said to be completely efficacious upon one application, and there are several testimonials to that effect on the wrapper from some of our most eminent native divines. I shall leave it here for you by the bedroom candles, and will be happy to supply you with more should you require it." With these words the United States Minister laid the bottle down on a marble table, and, closing his door, retired to rest.

For a moment the Canterville ghost stood quite motionless in natural indignation; then, dashing the bottle violently upon the polished floor, he fled down the corridor, uttering hollow groans, and emitting a ghastly green light. Just, however, as he reached the top of the great oak staircase, a door was flung open, two little white-robed figures appeared, and a large pillow whizzed past his head! There was evidently no time to be lost, so, hastily adopting the Fourth Dimension of Space as a means of escape; he vanished through the wainscoting, and the house became quite quiet.

by Oscar Wilde

The Ratcatcher

He looked up at me, a quick surreptitious glance, then over at Claude. His nose-end twitched, sniffing the air. He raised himself up and down a few times on his toes, swaying gently, and in a soft voice and secretive, he said: "Want to see somethin'?" He was obviously trying to retrieve his reputation.

"What?"

"Want to see somethin' *amazin'*?" As he said this he put his right hand into the deep poacher's pocket of his jacket and brought out a large live rat clasped tight between his fingers.

"Good God!"

"Ah! That's it, y'see!" He was crouching slightly now and craning his neck forward and leering at us and holding this enormous brown rat in his hands, one finger and thumb making a tight circle around the creature's neck, clamping its head rigid so it couldn't turn and bite.

"D'you usually carry rats around in your pockets?"

"Always got a rat or two about me somewhere."

With that he put his free hand into the other pocket and produced a small white ferret.

"Ferret," he said, holding it up by the neck.

The ferret seemed to know him and stayed still in his grasp.

"There's nothin'll kill a rat quicker'n a ferret. And there's nothin' a rat's more frightened of either."

He brought his hands close together in front of him so that the ferret's nose was within six inches of the rat's face. The pink beady eyes of the ferret stared at the rat. The rat struggled, trying to edge away from the killer.

"Now," he said. "Watch!"

by Roald Dahl

Noughts and Crosses

I glanced at my watch, wondering where Callum had got to. I turned, almost as if thinking about Callum would conjure him up. I gasped. Callum was standing right behind me, his appearance so sudden that he might've been a ghost, able to appear and disappear at will. And he looked so different. He'd shot up like a beanstalk. He was lean now, rather than skinny. He'd definitely sprouted muscles! And his dark cords and leather jacket made him look... mysterious somehow. His hair was longer too, almost shoulder-length. It suited him. Everything about him seemed different. Callum the boy had disappeared and in his place... I smiled, chiding myself. It was as if I'd expected time to stand still for him. I'm glad it hadn't though! Had I changed as much? I guess I must've.

"Good sneaking!" I congratulated him with a wry smile.

Slipping on my sandals, I stepped forward, my arms outstretched for a hug. I expected a similar jovial reply in greeting, but he didn't even smile. And even in this light, I could tell something was wrong. My arms dropped to my sides.

"Callum?"

Callum stepped forward and kissed me. A brief, icy-cold kiss on the lips. He stepped away from me, his eyes filled with regret. And then I saw them behind him. Four of them. Four noughts. Walking towards us. Towards me. A quick glance at Callum. Shock on my face. Confirmation, resignation on his. And I didn't wait to see any more. I turned and ran.

by Malorie Blackman

A Pack of Lies

"Time was only invented by clockmakers, and 'tis only kept by clocks! Well, I'll have none of it in my house! I'll have none of it, see! I'll put a stop to your murderous tick-tocking! You shan't count me out like some old boxer on the canvas!"

It was one minute to midnight.

Dragging the basket chair to the foot of the clock, Finbar turfed out the cushions and climbed up. A heavier man would have put his feet through the wickerwork, but Finbar was a jockey and as light as a whippet. He fumbled at the fastenings of the glass clock-face, and it flew open just as the chain-strung mechanism heaved up its chain like a ship weighing anchor. There was a click and a whirring of springs. Finbar put his finger to the minute hand and forced it backwards.

(Foolish man. He need only have stopped the pendulum.)

The chime mechanism was already triggered. It clanked and churned, and the whole frame juddered. Face to face with the staring dial, Finbar felt the noise of the first chime like a punch on the nose. He reeled sideways, caught his ear on the catch of the clock-face, and snatched his head away in pain.

The basket chair, unnerved by his curses, slid away from beneath him so that Finbar was pitched forward and embraced the great jarring shoulders of the chiming clock. The clock swayed forwards eagerly. Its door fell open, its chain and pendulum and rods and counterweights and chimes spilled out. Fatally wounded, the grandfather clock crashed down on its face.

Beneath it lay a few wicker twigs – the remnants of the basket chair – and Lucky Finbar, terror of the bookies, darling of the fairies – and the most superstitious old fool in the history of all Ireland.

by Geraldine McCaughrean

GRADE SIX – VERSE

Snow in the Suburbs

Every branch big with it,
Bent every twig with it;
Every fork like a white web-foot;
Every street and pavement mute:
Some flakes have lost their way,
    and grope back upward, when
Meeting those meandering down
    they turn and descend again.
The palings are glued together like a wall,
And there is no waft of wind with the fleecy fall.

A sparrow enters the tree,
Whereon immediately
A snow-lump thrice his own slight size
Descends on him and showers his head and eyes,
And overturns him,
And near inurns him,
And lights on a nether twig, when its brush
Starts off a volley of other lodging lumps with a rush.

The steps are a blanched slope,
Up which, with feeble hope,
A black cat comes, wide-eyed and thin;
And we take him in.

by Thomas Hardy

Antarctica

"I am just going outside and may be some time."
The others nod, pretending not to know.
At the heart of the ridiculous, the sublime.

He leaves them reading and begins to climb,
Goading his ghost into the howling snow;
He is just going outside and may be some time.

The tent recedes beneath its crust of rime
And frostbite is replaced by vertigo:
At the heart of the ridiculous, the sublime.

Need we consider it some sort of crime,
This numb self-sacrifice of the weakest? No,
He is just going outside and may be some time –

In fact, for ever. Solitary enzyme,
Though the night yield no glimmer there will glow,
At the heart of the ridiculous, the sublime.

He takes leave of the earthly pantomime
Quietly, knowing it is time to go.
"I am just going outside and may be some time."
At the heart of the ridiculous, the sublime.

by Derek Mahon

Epitaph for an Elderly Actress

She got in a rage
About age
And retired, in a huff, from the stage.
Which, taken all round, was a pity
Because she was still fairly pretty
But she got in a rage
About age.

She burst into tears
It appears
When the rude, inconsiderate years
Undermined her once flawless complexion
And whenever she saw her reflection
In a mirror, she burst into tears
It appears.

She got in a state
About weight
And resented each morsel she ate.
Her colon she constantly sluiced
And reduced and reduced and reduced
And, at quite an incredible rate
Put on weight.

She got in a rage
About age
But she still could have played Mistress Page
And she certainly could have done worse
Than *Hay Fever* or *Juliet's Nurse*
But she got in a terrible rage
About age.

And she moaned and she wept and she wailed
And she roared and she ranted and railed
And retired, very heavily, veiled,
From the stage.

by Noël Coward

Conversation with a Survivor

What did you do in those days
that you shouldn't have done?
"Nothing"

What did you not do
that you should have done?
"This and that:
a few things"

Why did you not do it?
"Because I was afraid"
Why were you afraid?
"Because I didn't want to die"

Did others die
because you didn't want to?
"I think
they did"

Have you got anything else to say
about what you didn't do?
"Yes: to ask you
what you would have done in my place?"

I do not know
and cannot sit in judgement on you.
Only one thing I know:
Tomorrow none of us
will stay alive
if today
we again do nothing

by Erich Fried, translated by Stuart Hood

The Highwayman (Part One)

The wind was a torrent of darkness among the gusty trees,
The moon was a ghostly galleon tossed upon cloudy seas,
The road was a ribbon of moonlight over the purple moor,
And the highwayman came riding –
   Riding – riding –
The highwayman came riding, up to the old inn-door.

He'd a French cocked-hat on his forehead, a bunch of lace at
   his chin,
A coat of the claret velvet, and breeches of brown doeskin:
They fitted with never a wrinkle; his boots were up to the
   thigh!
And he rode with a jewelled twinkle,
   His pistol butts a-twinkle,
His rapier hilt a-twinkle, under the jewelled sky.

Over the cobbles he clattered and clashed in the dark inn-
   yard,
And he tapped with his whip on the shutters, but all was
   locked and barred:
He whistled a tune to the window; and who should be waiting
   there
But the landlord's black-eyed daughter
   Bess, the landlord's daughter,
Plaiting a dark red love-knot into her long black hair.

And dark in the dark old inn-yard a stable-wicket creaked
Where Tim, the ostler, listened; his face was white and
   peaked,
His eyes were hollows of madness, his hair like mouldy hay;
But he loved the landlord's daughter,
   The landlord's red-lipped daughter:
Dumb as a dog he listened, and he heard the robber say –

"One kiss, my bonny sweetheart, I'm after a prize tonight,
But I shall be back with the yellow gold before the morning

light.
Yet if they press me sharply, and harry me through the day,
Then look for me by moonlight,
    Watch for me by moonlight:
I'll come to thee by moonlight, though Hell should bar the
    way."

He rose upright in the stirrups, he scarce could reach her
    hand;
But she loosened her hair i' the casement! His face burnt like
    a brand
As the black cascade of perfume came tumbling over his
    breast;
And he kissed its waves in the moonlight,
    (Oh, sweet black waves in the moonlight)
Then he tugged at his reins in the moonlight, and galloped
    away to the West.

by Alfred Noyes

India

They hunt, the velvet tigers in the jungle,
The spotted jungle full of shapeless patches –
Sometimes they're leaves, sometimes they're hanging
flowers,
Sometimes they're hot gold patches of the sun:
They hunt, the velvet tigers in the jungle!

What do they hunt by glimmering pools of water,
By the round silver Moon, the Pool of Heaven –
In the striped grass, amid the barkless trees –
The stars scattered like eyes of beasts above them!

What do they hunt, their hot breath scorching insects,
Insects that blunder blindly in the way,
Vividly fluttering – they also are hunting,
Are glittering with a tiny ecstasy!

The grass is flaming and the trees are growing,
The very mud is gurgling in the pools,
Green toads are watching, crimson parrots flying,
Two pairs of eyes meet one another glowing –
They hunt, the velvet tigers in the jungle.

by W J Turner

Swim Right Up To Me

I first learnt to swim at home in my father's study
On the piano-stool, planted on the middle of the rug.
Stomach down, head up, arms and legs rowing hard;
I swam bravely, ploughing up the small room,
Pinned on a crushed stuckness of stomach to tapestry,
The twin handles hard on my elbows on the back-stroke.
A view down through four braced wooden legs
To the same thin spot in the rug.
My mother faced me, calling rhythmic encouragement,
Almost stepping back to let me swim up to her,
Reminding me to breathe;
And wiping my hair and eyes with her hand
As I swam and swam on the furniture against a running tide,
Pig-cheeked, concentrating on pushing and pushing away,
Planning to learn to fly next, easy,
Higher than the kitchen table, even. The garden wall.

by Katherine Pierpoint

Anthem for Doomed Youth

What passing-bells for these who die as cattle?
 – Only the monstrous anger of the guns.
Only the stuttering rifles' rapid rattle
Can patter out their hasty orisons.
No mockeries now for them; no prayers nor bells;
Nor any voice of mourning save the choirs, –
The shrill, demented choirs of wailing shells;
And bugles calling for them from sad shires.

What candles may be held to speed them all?
Not in the hands of boys but in their eyes
Shall shine the holy glimmers of goodbyes.
The pallor of girls' brows shall be their pall;
Their flowers the tenderness of patient minds,
And each slow dusk a drawing-down of blinds.

by Wilfred Owen

GRADE SIX – PROSE

Hullabaloo in the Guava Orchard

Sampath looked at his father. Could he be hearing correctly?

Seeing Sampath's face, Mr Chawla was filled with irritation. What a ridiculous look of overdone incredulity! "And you had better start learning some philosophy and religion," he said. "People will soon get tired if you cannot converse on a deeper level. I will buy you a copy of the Vedas. You really cannot sit saying silly things for ever."

The monkeys threw apples at Mr Chawla's head for fun, though it looked as if they were attempting to protect Sampath. He gestured angrily at them, but they greeted his protest with a barrage of bananas. Mr Chawla lost his temper.

"They are making a mockery of us," he said, his sense of dignity hurt. "It is getting too much. People will think you are a circus act. Sitting in the tree with drunken monkeys! We must put you in a proper building immediately."

"I am not going to live anywhere but in this tree," said Sampath. "And the monkeys are not drunk right now. They are only playing."

When his father had gone he realized his heart was thumping. He could not get the horrible thought out of his mind. Leave his tree? Never. Never ever, he thought, his body trembling with indignation. Fiercely, he studied the branch in front of him. He and his father were as different as black from white, as chickens from potatoes, as peas from buckets.

by Kiran Desai

Life of Pi

I realized with horror that the tanker was not simply coming our way – it was in fact bearing down on us. The bow was a vast wall of metal that was getting wider every second. A huge wave girdling it was advancing towards us relentlessly. Richard Parker finally sensed the looming juggernaut. He turned and went "Woof! Woof!" but not doglike – it was tigerlike: powerful, scary and utterly suited to the situation.

"Richard Parker, it's going to run us over! What are we going to do? Quick, quick, a flare! No! Must row. Oar in oarlock…there! *HUMPF! HUMPF! HUMPF! HUMPF! HUMPF! HUM–*"

The bow wave pushed us up. Richard Parker crouched, and the hairs on him stood up. The lifeboat slid off the bow wave and missed the tanker by less than two feet.

The ship slid by for what seemed like a mile, a mile of high, black canyon wall, a mile of castle fortification with not a single sentinel to notice us languishing in the moat. I fired off a rocket flare, but I aimed it poorly. Instead of surging over the bulwarks and exploding in the captain's face, it ricocheted off the ship's side and went straight into the Pacific, where it died with a hiss. I blew on my whistle with all my might. I shouted at the top of my lungs. All to no avail.

Its engines rumbling loudly and its propellers chopping explosively underwater, the ship churned past us and left us bouncing and bobbing in its frothy wake. After so many weeks of natural sounds, these mechanical noises were strange and awesome and stunned me into silence.

by Yann Martel

Eragon

Without warning, the doors swung outward on hidden joints. As the rift widened between them, rays of sunlight streamed into the tunnel, falling on Saphira and Eragon. Temporarily blinded, Eragon blinked and squinted. When his eyes adjusted to the light, he gasped.

They were inside a massive volcanic crater. Its walls narrowed to a small ragged opening so high above that Eragon could not judge the distance – it might have been more than a dozen miles. A soft beam of light fell through the aperture, illuminating the crater's centre, though it left the rest of the cavernous expanse in hushed twilight.

The crater's far side, hazy blue in the distance, looked to be nearly ten miles away. Giant icicles hundreds of feet thick and thousands of feet long hung leagues above them like glistening daggers. Eragon knew from his experience in the valley that no one, not even Saphira, could reach those lofty points. Farther down the crater's inner walls, dark mats of moss and lichen covered the rock.

He lowered his gaze and saw a wide cobblestone path extending from the doors' threshold. The path ran straight to the centre of the crater, where it ended at the base of a snowy-white mountain that glittered like an uncut gem with thousands of coloured lights. It was less than a tenth of the height of the crater that loomed over and around it, but its diminutive appearance was deceiving, for it was slightly higher than a mile.

Long as it was, the tunnel had only taken them through one side of the crater wall. As Eragon stared, he heard Orik say deeply, "Look well, human, for no Rider has set eyes upon this for nigh over a hundred years. The airy peak under which we stand is Farthen Dûr – discovered thousands of years ago by the father of our race, Korgan, while he tunnelled for gold. And in the centre stands our greatest achievement: Tronjheim, the city-mountain built from the purest marble." The doors grated to a halt.

A city!

by Christopher Paolini

Young Men in Spats

The girl Dahlia during these exchanges had been sitting on a sofa at the end of the room, turning the pages of a weekly paper, and the sight of her drew Freddie like a magnet. Her womanly sympathy was just what he felt he could do with at this juncture. Treading with infinite caution, he crossed to where she sat: and, having scanned the terrain narrowly for cats, sank down on the sofa at her side. And conceive his agony of spirit when he discovered that womanly sympathy had been turned off at the main. The girl was like a chunk of ice cream with spikes all over it.

"Please do not trouble to explain," she said coldly, in answer to his opening words. "I quite understand that there are people who have this odd dislike of animals."

"But, dash it…" cried Freddie, waving his arm in a frenzied sort of way. "Oh, I say, sorry," he added, as his fist sloshed another of the menagerie in the short ribs.

Dahlia caught the animal as it flew through the air.

"I think perhaps you had better take Augustus, Mother," she said. "He seems to be annoying Mr Widgeon."

"Quite," said Lady Prenderby. "He will be safer with me."

"But, dash it…" bleated Freddie.

Dahlia Prenderby drew in her breath sharply.

"How true it is," she said, "that one never really knows a man till after one has seen him in one's own home."

"What do you mean by that?"

"Oh, nothing," said Dahlia Prenderby.

She rose and moved to the piano, where she proceeded to sing old Breton folksongs in a distant manner, leaving Freddie to make out as best he could with a family album containing faded photographs with 'Aunt Emmy bathing at Llandudno, 1893', and 'This is Cousin George at the fancy-dress ball' written under them.

And so the long, quiet, peaceful home evening wore on, till eventually Lady Prenderby mercifully blew the whistle and he was at liberty to sneak off to his bedroom.

by P G Wodehouse

The Lollipop Shoes

My last public persona was Françoise Lavery, a teacher of English at the Lycée Rousseau in the 11th. Age thirty-two; born in Nantes; married and widowed in the same year to Raoul Lavery, killed in a car crash on the eve of the anniversary – a rather romantic touch, I thought, that explained her faint air of melancholy. A strict vegetarian, rather shy, diligent, but not talented enough to be a threat. All in all, a nice girl – which just goes to show you should never judge by appearances.

Today, however, I'm someone else. Twenty-five thousand euros is no small sum, and there's always the chance that someone will begin to suspect the truth. Most people don't – most people wouldn't notice a crime if it was going on right in front of them – but I haven't got this far by taking risks, and I've found that it's safer to stay on the move.

So I travel light – a battered leather case and a Sony laptop containing the makings of over a hundred possible identities – and I can be packed, cleaned out, all traces gone in rather less than an afternoon.

That's how Françoise disappeared. I burnt her papers, correspondence, bank details, notes. I closed all accounts in her name. Books, clothes, furniture and the rest, I gave to the Croix Rouge. It never pays to gather moss.

After that I needed to find myself anew. I booked into a cheap hotel, paid on Amélie's credit card, changed out of Emma's clothes and went shopping.

Françoise was a dowdy type; sensible heels and neat chignons. My new persona, however, has a different style. Zozie de l'Alba is her name – she is vaguely foreign, though you might be hard pressed to tell her country of origin. She's as flamboyant as Françoise was not – wears costume jewellery in her hair; loves bright colours and frivolous shapes; favours bazaars and vintage shops, and would never be seen dead in sensible shoes.

by Joanne Harris

I am a cloud, I can blow anywhere

"Mulumbe, Mulumbe," someone was calling me in my sleep. "Mulumbe, Mulumbe." The call became a cry. "Mulumbe, wake up!" Curling into a ball I tried to shrug off whoever it was jolting me from my delicious rest. But the voice would not stop. It grew more insistent. It began to shout. "Mulumbe, you must wake up now!"

I opened my eyes. Grandmother was leaning over me. She was shaking my shoulder. "They are coming," she said.

I could hear the terror in her voice. There was no need for any questions. I got up and followed her outside.

"Quick, child," she urged.

"What about the others, Grandmother?"

"I will wake the others. Run, before it's too late!"

It was still dark and the earth was cold beneath my bare feet. Dressed only in my T-shirt and skirt, I shivered. Quickly the rest of the family emerged from their huts and Grandmother shepherded them into the forest. All at once the night was filled with shouts and screams. *They* had come.

It was mayhem, as though the whole village had become one of the ants' nests that my little brothers liked to poke with sticks. People scattered in all directions. Bumping into one another, they plunged shrieking into the trees.

At that moment a hand grasped mine. "Mulumbe, what are you still doing here?" Grandmother half-screamed.

"Are all the others safe?" I asked.

"Yes, but now *you* are going to be caught."

We ran blindly, lunging through the thick, thorny trees. Barbs lacerated my T-shirt and arms, and tugged at my hair like talons grappling to stop us. Crashing through the bush like warthogs, we thought only of escape.

by Jonathan and Shirley Tulloch

The Withered Arm

Rhoda sat a long time over the turf ashes that she had raked out in front of her to extinguish them. She contemplated so intently the new wife, as presented to her in her mind's eye over the embers, that she forgot the lapse of time. At last, wearied with her day's work, she too retired.

But the figure which had occupied her so much during this and the previous days was not to be banished at night. For the first time Gertrude Lodge visited the supplanted woman in her dreams. Rhoda Brook dreamed – since her assertion that she really saw, before falling asleep, was not to be believed – that the young wife, in the pale silk dress and white bonnet, but with features shockingly distorted, and wrinkled as by age, was sitting upon her chest as she lay. The pressure of Mrs Lodge's person grew heavier; the blue eyes peered cruelly into her face; and then the figure thrust forward its left hand mockingly, so as to make the wedding-ring it wore glitter in Rhoda's eyes. Maddened mentally, and nearly suffocated by pressure, the sleeper struggled; the incubus, still regarding her, withdrew to the foot of the bed, only, however, to come forward by degrees, resume her seat, and flash her left hand as before.

Gasping for breath, Rhoda, in a last desperate effort, swung out her right hand, seized the confronting spectre by its obtrusive left arm, and whirled it backward to the floor, starting up herself as she did so with a low cry.

"Oh, merciful heaven!" she cried, sitting on the edge of the bed in a cold sweat, "that was not a dream – she was here!"

She could feel her antagonist's arm within her grasp even now – the very flesh and bone of it, as it seemed. She looked on the floor whither she had whirled the spectre, but there was nothing to be seen.

by Thomas Hardy

The Life and Times of the Thunderbolt Kid

Dr Brewster was the most unnerving dentist in America. He was, for one thing, about a hundred and eight years old and had more than a hint of Parkinsonism in his wobbly hands. Nothing about him inspired confidence. He was perennially surprised by the power of his own equipment. "Whoa!" he'd say as he briefly enlivened some screaming device or other. "You could do some damage with *that*, I bet!"

Worse still, he didn't believe in novocaine. He thought it dangerous and unproven. When Dr Brewster, humming mindlessly, drilled through rocky molar and found the pulpy mass of tender nerve within, it could make your toes burst out the front of your shoes.

We appeared to be his only patients. I used to wonder why my father put us through this seasonal nightmare, and then I heard Dr Brewster congratulating him one day on his courageous frugality and I understood at once, for my father was the twentieth century's cheapest man. "There's no point in putting yourself to the danger and expense of novocaine for anything less than the whole or partial removal of a jaw," Dr Brewster was saying.

"Absolutely," my father agreed. Actually he said something more like "Abmmffffmmfff," as he had just stepped from Dr Brewster's chair and wouldn't be able to speak intelligibly for at least three days, but he nodded with feeling.

"I wish more people felt like you, Mr Bryson," Dr Brewster added. "That will be three dollars, please."

by Bill Bryson

GRADE SEVEN – VERSE

The Right Word

Outside the door,
lurking in the shadows,
is a terrorist.

Is that the wrong description?
Outside that door,
taking shelter in the shadows,
is a freedom-fighter.

I haven't got this right.
Outside, waiting in the shadows,
is a hostile militant.

Are words no more
than waving, wavering flags?
Outside your door,
watchful in the shadows,
is a guerrilla warrior.

God help me.
Outside, defying every shadow,
stands a martyr.
I saw his face.

No words can help me now.
Just outside the door,
lost in shadows,
is a child who looks like mine.

One word for you.
Outside my door,
his hand too steady,
his eyes too hard
is a boy who looks like your son, too.

I open the door.
Come in, I say.
Come in and eat with us.

The child steps in
and carefully, at my door,
takes off his shoes.

by Imtiaz Dharker

The Telephone Call

They asked me, "Are you sitting down?
Right? This is Universal Lotteries,"
they said. "You've won the top prize,
the Ultra-super Global Special.
What would you do with a million pounds?
Or, actually, with more than a million –
not that it makes a lot of difference
once you're a millionaire." And they laughed.

"Are you OK?" they asked – "Still there?
Come on, now, tell us, how does it feel?"
I said, "I just… I can't believe it!"
They said, "That's what they all say.
What else? Go on, tell us about it."
I said, "I feel the top of my head
has floated off, out through the window,
revolving like a flying saucer."

"That's unusual," they said. "Go on."
I said, "I'm finding it hard to talk.
My throat's gone dry, my nose is tingling.
I think I'm going to sneeze – or cry."
"That's right," they said, "don't be ashamed
of giving way to your emotions.
It isn't every day you hear
you're going to get a million pounds.

Relax, now, have a little cry;
we'll give you a moment…" "Hang on!" I said.
"I haven't bought a lottery ticket
for years and years. And what did you say
the company's called?" They laughed again.
"Not to worry about a ticket.
We're Universal. We operate
a retrospective Chances Module.

Nearly everyone's bought a ticket
in some lottery or another,
once at least. We buy up the files,
feed the names into our computer,
and see who the lucky person is."
"Well, that's incredible," I said.
"It's marvellous. I still can't quite…
I'll believe it when I see the cheque."

"Oh," they said, "there's no cheque."
"But the money?" "We don't deal in money.
Experiences are what we deal in.
You've had a great experience, right?
Exciting? Something you'll remember?
That's your prize. So congratulations
from all of us at Universal.
Have a nice day!" And the line went dead.

by Fleur Adcock

Sand Artist

On the damp seashore
above dark rainbows of shells, seaweed, seacoal,
the sandman wanders, seeking for a pitch.

Ebb tide is his time. The sands are lonely,
but a few lost families
camp for the day on its Easter emptiness.

He seeks the firm dark sand of the retreating waves.
– With their sandwiches and flasks of tea, they
lay their towels on the dry slopes of dunes.

From the sea's edge he draws his pail
of bitter brine, and bears it carefully
towards the place of first creation.

There he begins his labours. Silent,
not looking up at passing shadows
of curious children, he moulds his dreams.

Not simple sandcastles, melting as they dry,
but galleons, anchors, dolphins, cornucopias of fish,
mermaids, Neptunes, dragons of the deep.

With a piece of stick, a playing card
and the blunt fingers of a working man
the artist resurrects existence from the sea.

And as the returning tide takes back its gifts,
he waits in silence by his pitman's cap
for pennies from the sky.

by James Kirkup

Yew Tree Guest House

In guest-house lounges
elderly ladies shrivel away
wearing bright beads and jumpers
to colour the waiting day
between breakfast and bed.

Grey widows whose beds and meals are made,
husbands tidied with the emptied cupboards,
live in mortgaged time
disguising inconsequence
with shavings of surface talk, letters
to nieces, stitches dropped in the quick-knit jacket,
picked up for makeweight meaning.

Weekdays are patterned by meals –
sole chance for speculation –
will it be cabbage or peas; boiled fish or fried?
Dead Sunday is dedicated to roast beef –
knives and forks are grips upon existence.
This diversion lengthens the journey;
and since Mrs Porter ceased to come downstairs,
ceased altogether,
the ladies at the Yew Tree Guest House
draw closer to the table.

by Phoebe Hesketh

Dress Rehearsals

On the final night of Carnivale, headlights
swarm down the hill like lava
making brief beds of moving embers
you can almost hear the night extinguishing.
Darkness slides over itself, drawing down
each of its blinds, then – even more slowly –
opening them, and the world returns
as a slur of ash and rumour, birds
calling out their names to themselves,
repeating their lines in their grey and hidden rooms.

How many more days of twilight, nightfall, dawn?
How many seasons flicked through
like frames in a cine-film, till the loose celluloid spins
tickering on the spool? The summers stall
in the machine and burn up; winter is a white wall.
Unjammed, the projector freewheels; years lurch
untangling: the fast-forward trees
sprawling, in a week, from bud-burst to leaf-fall.
How much more of this life and death,
and these, their beautiful endless dress rehearsals?

by Robin Robertson

Mother-in-law

Such a nice girl. Just what I wanted
For the boy. Not top drawer, you know,
But so often, in our position, that
Turns out to be a mistake. They get
The ideas of their station, and that upsets
So many applecarts. The lieges, of course,
Are particularly hidebound, and the boy,
For all his absentminded ways, is a great one
For convention. Court mourning, you know...
Things like that. We don't want a Brunhilde
Here. But she was so suitable. Devoted
To her father and brother, and,
Of course, to the boy. And a very
Respectable, loyal family. Well, loyal
To number two, at any rate. Number one,
I remember, never quite trusted... Yes,
And had just the right interests. Folk song, for instance,
(Such a sweet little voice), and amateur
Dramatics. Inherited *that* taste
From her father. Dear old fellow, he'd go on
For hours about his college drama group.
And the boy's so keen on the stage. It's nice
When husband and wife have a shared interest,
Don't you think? Then botany. Poor little soul,
She was really keen. We'd go for trips
With the vasculum, and have such fun
Asking the lieges their country names for flowers.
Some of them, my dear, were scarcely delicate
(The names, I mean), but the young nowadays
Don't seem to notice. Marriage
Would have made her more innocent, of course.
I can't think who will do for the boy now.
I seem to be the only woman left round here.

by U A Fanthorpe

Blackberrying

Nobody in the lane, and nothing, nothing but blackberries,
Blackberries on either side, though on the right mainly,
A blackberry alley, going down in hooks, and a sea
Somewhere at the end of it, heaving. Blackberries
Big as the ball of my thumb, and dumb as eyes
Ebon in the hedges, fat
With blue-red juices. These they squander on my fingers.
I had not asked for such a blood sisterhood; they must love
    me.
They accommodate themselves to my milkbottle, flattening
    their sides.

Overhead go the choughs in black, cacophonous flocks –
Bits of burnt paper wheeling in a blown sky.
Theirs is the only voice, protesting, protesting.
I do not think the sea will appear at all.
The high, green meadows are glowing, as if lit from within.
I come to one bush of berries so ripe it is a bush of flies,
Hanging their bluegreen bellies and their wing panes in a
    Chinese screen.
The honey-feast of the berries has stunned them; they believe
    in heaven.
One more hook, and the berries and bushes end.

The only thing to come now is the sea.
From between two hills a sudden wind funnels at me,
Slapping its phantom laundry in my face.
These hills are too green and sweet to have tasted salt.
I follow the sheep path between them. A last hook brings me
To the hills' northern face, and the face is orange rock
That looks out on nothing, nothing but a great space
Of white and pewter lights, and a din like silversmiths
Beating and beating at an intractable metal.

by Sylvia Plath

When I Dance

When I dance it isn't merely
That music absorbs my shyness,
My laughter settles in my eyes,
My swings of arms convert my frills
As timing tunes my feet with floor
As if I never just looked on.

It is that when I dance
O music expands my hearing
And it wants no mathematics,
It wants no thinking, no speaking,
It only wants all my feeling
In with animation of place.

When I dance it isn't merely
That surprises dictate movements,
Other rhythms move my rhythms,
I uncradle rocking-memory
And skipping, hopping and running
All mix movements I balance in.

It is that when I dance
I'm costumed in a rainbow mood,
I'm okay at any angle,
Outfit of drums crowds madness round,
Talking winds and plucked strings conspire,
Beat after beat warms me like sun.

When I dance it isn't merely
I shift bodyweight balances
As movement amasses my show,
I celebrate each dancer here,
No sleep invades me now at all
And I see how I am tireless.

It is that when I dance
I gather up all my senses
Well into hearing and feeling,
With body's flexible postures
Telling their poetry in movement
And I celebrate all rhythms.

by James Berry

GRADE SEVEN – PROSE

Great Expectations

In an arm-chair, with an elbow resting on the table and her head leaning on that hand, sat the strangest lady I have ever seen, or shall ever see.

She was dressed in rich materials – satins, and lace, and silks – all of white. Her shoes were white. And she had a long white veil dependent from her hair, and she had bridal flowers in her hair, but her hair was white. Some bright jewels sparkled on her neck and on her hands, and some other jewels lay sparkling on the table. Dresses, less splendid than the dress she wore, and half-packed trunks, were scattered about. She had not quite finished dressing, for she had but one shoe on – the other was on the table near her hand – her veil was but half-arranged, her watch and chain were not put on, and some lace for her bosom lay with those trinkets, and with her handkerchief, and gloves, and some flowers, and a Prayer-book, all confusedly heaped about the looking-glass.

It was not in the first few moments that I saw all these things, though I saw more of them in the first moments than might be supposed. But, I saw that everything within my view which ought to be white had been white long ago, and had lost its lustre, and was faded and yellow. I saw that the bride within the bridal dress had withered like the dress, and like the flowers, and had no brightness left but the brightness of her sunken eyes. I saw that the dress had been put upon the rounded figure of a young woman, and that the figure upon which it now hung loose, had shrunk to skin and bone. Once, I had been taken to see some ghastly waxwork at the Fair, representing I know not what impossible personage lying in state. Once, I had been taken to one of our old marsh churches to see a skeleton in the ashes of a rich dress, that had been dug out of a vault under the church pavement. Now, waxwork and skeleton seemed to have dark eyes that moved and looked at me. I should have cried out, if I could.

"Who is it?" said the lady at the table.

"Pip, ma'am."

"Pip?"

"Mr Pumblechook's boy, ma'am. Come – to play."

"Come nearer; let me look at you. Come close."

by Charles Dickens

The Other Side of the Dale

Mine wasn't quite such 'a nice surprise' a few moments later. I returned to my car and opened the boot to take the books and equipment into the Centre – only to find everything a complete jumble. In the very middle of the mess crouched the pheasant I had run over and had assumed was dead. It was, to my amazement, very much alive and kicking. Connie returned to the entrance just in time to see something squawking and pecking and fluttering its wings madly. I had stunned the creature, not killed it; now fully recovered, it was not at all pleased to have been incarcerated in the cramped dark boot of a car for a couple of hours, bumping along mile after mile.

"Shoo!" I cried, trying to encourage the bird to leave the boot, but every time my hand came within pecking range it lunged at me. "Shoo! Shoo!" I exclaimed again. Then, turning, I realized I had attracted a crowd of interested teachers who stood in a half circle with Connie, watching proceedings.

"Not wild animals now," wailed Connie. "You know I can't stand the stuffed variety that Mr Clamp brings into the Centre, never mind savage beasts!"

"Is it a visual aid?" asked one teacher mischievously.

"No, it is not!" I snapped.

"Are we going to write bird poems," asked another teacher chuckling, "from first-hand experience?"

"No, we are not!" came my angry reply.

"Well, I don't want it in the Centre," said Connie. "I'm not cleaning up after that. I have enough trouble with the stuffed heron."

"It's not going in the Centre, Connie," I said getting as flustered as the bird. The bird made another loud, plaintive squawk and beat its wings and thrashed its tail.

"What sort of bird is it?" asked Connie peering through the dusky evening light.

Before I could answer, Miss Pilkington, who was now amongst the amused onlookers, responded. "Oh, I should say aggressive," she said with a twinkle in her eyes. "Wouldn't you, Mr Phinn?"

by Gervase Phinn

The Riddler's Gift

The night was dark, thick with dreadful secrets. The fire crackled sullenly in its hearth, its light framed the window with a dull red glow. Off in the distance, Tabitha heard a nightjar screaming its nocturnal sermon. She tried to calm her breathing.

A face lunged out of the darkness beyond the window. The glass swirled out of focus, the roof and walls and floor spun, but in the centre of the sudden confusion the attacker's face was as clear as etched stone. His cold, marbled eyes were grey, stained with yellow. She knew those eyes, they pierced Tabitha to the bone. Then he struck the glass with his forearms and the window exploded.

Vicious shards splintered over her body. A thousand tiny teeth bit her. The fear was like a wall, so solid that it drove her backwards, reeling. She felt naked and helpless. The window was empty. The Shadowcaster hadn't jumped into the room. He had vanished.

Blood welled up from cuts in her face and scalp and soaked into the collar of her woollen jacket. She turned, violated, toward her parents.

"You will not touch my child!" her father roared at the night beyond the shattered window. A cold breeze pushed into the room, rippling the curtain. The Shadowcaster was gone.

"No!" her father roared again. He ran to the window, crushing the shattered glass underfoot. He looked capable of tearing down a tree with his bare hands, so angry was he. He cleared the jagged shards from the bottom of the frame with a sweep of his boot, and leapt out into the dark night. The top of the window remained like a fringe of broken teeth. Her father thudded to the ground below.

Her mother issued a strangled cry after her father, but he was gone, running away in pursuit. She went to the gaping exit, but then she froze and recoiled.

A dark shape suddenly filled the window. The Shadowcaster dropped from the windowsill to the floor, and surged into the room, pushing her mother backwards with the threat of his presence. His black cloak swirled wide, preventing escape.

by Greg Hamerton

A Room with a View

"Nothing ever happens to me," she reflected, as she entered the Piazza Signoria and looked nonchalantly at its marvels, now fairly familiar to her. The great square was in shadow; the sunshine had come too late to strike it. Neptune was already unsubstantial in the twilight, half god, half ghost, and his fountain splashed dreamily to the men and satyrs who idled together on its marge. The Loggia showed as the triple entrance of a cave, wherein dwelt many a deity, shadowy but immortal, looking forth upon the arrivals and departures of mankind. It was the hour of unreality – the hour, that is, when unfamiliar things are real. An older person at such an hour and in such a place might think that sufficient was happening to him, and rest content. Lucy desired more.

Then something did happen.

Two Italians by the Loggia had been bickering about a debt. "Cinque lire," they had cried, "cinque lire!" They sparred at each other, and one of them was hit lightly upon the chest. He frowned; he bent towards Lucy with a look of interest, as if he had an important message for her. He opened his lips to deliver it, and a stream of red came out between them and trickled down his unshaven chin.

That was all. A crowd rose out of the dusk. It hid this extraordinary man from her, and bore him away to the fountain. Mr George Emerson happened to be a few paces away, looking at her across the spot where the man had been. How very odd! Across something. Even as she caught sight of him he grew dim; the palace itself grew dim, swayed above her, fell onto her softly, slowly, noiselessly, and the sky fell with it.

She thought: "Oh, what have I done?"

"Oh, what have I done?" she murmured, and opened her eyes.

George Emerson still looked at her, but not across anything. She had complained of dullness, and lo! one man was stabbed, and another held her in his arms.

They were sitting on some steps in the Uffizi Arcade. He must have carried her. He rose when she spoke, and began to dust his knees. She repeated:

"Oh, what have I done?"

"You fainted."

by E M Forster

Cider with Rosie

Beautiful Marge led the way up the path and rapped elegantly on Granny's door. Meanwhile Doth and Phyl hitched their slipping girdles, pushed the bandeaux out of their eyes, stood hands on hips making light conversation – two jazz-debs bright in the sun.

For once Granny Trill seemed hard of hearing, though the girls had knocked three times. So with a charming shrug and a fastidious sigh Marge swung a great kick at the door.

"Who's that?" came a frightened yelp from within.

"It's only us," trilled the girls.

They waltzed through the door, apparitions of rose, striking postures straight out of *Home Notes*. "How do we look then, Gran?" asked Marjorie. "This line is the mode, you know. We copied it out of that pattern book. It's the rage in Stroud, they say."

Riffling their feathers, arching their necks, catching coy reflections in mirrors, they paraded the room, three leggy flamingoes, each lit by a golden down. To me they were something out of the sky, airborne visions of fairy light; and with all the enthusiasm they were capable of they gave the old lady the works. Yet all was clearly not going well. There was a definite chill in the air....

Granny watched them awhile, then her jaws snapped shut; worse still, her gums stopped chewing. Then she clapped her hands with a terrible crack.

"You baggages! You jumped-up varmints! Be off, or I'll fetch me broom!"

The girls retreated at the dainty double, surprised but in no way insulted. Their sense of fashion was unassailable, for were they not up with the times? How could the old girl know about belts and bandeaux? – after all, she was only a peasant....

But later Gran Trill took our Mother aside and spoke grimly of her concern.

"You better watch them gels of yourn. They'll bring shame on us one of these days."

by Laurie Lee, adapted by James Roose-Evans

Every Man for Himself

The moment was almost upon us. The stern began to lift from the water. Guggenheim and his valet played mountaineers, going hand over hand up the rail. The hymn turned ragged; ceased altogether. The musicians scrambled upwards, the spike of the cello scraping the deck. Clinging to the rung of the ladder I tried to climb to the roof but there was such a sideways slant that I waved like a flag on a pole. I thought I must make a leap for it and turned to look for Hopper. Something, some inner voice urged me to glance below and I saw Scurra again, one arm hooked through the rail to steady himself. I raised my hand in greeting – then the water, first slithering, then tumbling, gushed us apart.

As the ship staggered and tipped, a great volume of water flowed in over the submerged bows and tossed me like a cork to the roof. Hopper was there too. My fingers touched some kind of bolt near the ventilation grille and I grabbed it tight. I filled my lungs with air and fixed my eyes on the blurred horizon, determined to hang on until I was sure I could float free rather than be swilled back and forth in a maelstrom. I wouldn't waste my strength in swimming, not yet, for I knew the ship was now my enemy and if I wasn't vigilant would drag me with her to the grave. I waited for the next slithering dip and when it came and the waves rushed in and swept me higher, I released my grip and let myself be carried away, over the tangle of ropes and wires and davits, clear of the rails and out into the darkness. I heard the angry roaring of the dying ship, the deafening cacophony as she stood on end and all her guts tore loose. I choked on soot and cringed beneath the sparks dancing like fire-flies as the forward funnel broke and smashed the sea in two. I thought I saw Hopper's face but one eye was ripped away and he gobbled like a fish on the hook. I was sucked under, as I knew I would be, down, down, and still I waited, waited until the pull slackened – then I struck out with all my strength.

by Beryl Bainbridge

Tobermory (The Chronicles of Clovis)

Sir Wilfrid went in search of the animal, and the company settled themselves down to the languid expectation of witnessing some more or less adroit drawing-room ventriloquism.

In a minute Sir Wilfrid was back in the room, his face white beneath its tan and his eyes dilated with excitement.

"By Gad, it's true!"

His agitation was unmistakably genuine, and his hearers started forward in a thrill of wakened interest.

Collapsing into an armchair he continued breathlessly:

"I found him dozing in the smoking-room, and called out to him to come for his tea. He blinked at me in his usual way, and I said, 'Come on, Toby; don't keep us waiting' and, by Gad! he drawled out in a most horribly natural voice that he'd come when he dashed well pleased! I nearly jumped out of my skin!"

Appin had preached to absolutely incredulous hearers; Sir Wilfrid's statement carried instant conviction. A Babel-like chorus of startled exclamation arose, amid which the scientist sat mutely enjoying the first fruit of his stupendous discovery.

In the midst of the clamour Tobermory entered the room and made his way with velvet tread and studied unconcern across the group seated round the tea-table.

A sudden hush of awkwardness and constraint fell on

the company. Somehow there seemed an element of embarrassment in addressing on equal terms a domestic cat of acknowledged dental ability.

"Will you have some milk, Tobermory?" asked Lady Blemley in a rather strained voice.

"I don't mind if I do," was the response, couched in a tone of even indifference. A shiver of suppressed excitement went through the listeners, and Lady Blemley might be excused for pouring out the saucerful of milk rather unsteadily.

"I'm afraid I've spilt a good deal of it," she said apologetically.

by Saki

If Nobody Speaks of Remarkable Things

So listen.

Listen, and there is more to hear.

The rattle of a dustbin lid knocked to the floor.

The scrawl and scratch of two hackle-raised cats.

The sudden thundercrash of bottles emptied into crates.

The slam-slam of car doors, the changing of gears, the hobbled clip-clop of a slow walk home.

The rippled roll of shutters pulled down on late-night cafes, a crackled voice crying street names for taxis, a loud scream that lingers and cracks into laughter, a bang that might just be an old car backfiring, a callbox calling out for an answer, a treeful of birds tricked into morning, a whistle and a shout and a broken glass, a blare of soft music and a blam of hard beats, a barking and yelling and singing and crying and it all swells up all the rumbles and crashes and bangings and slams, all the noise and the rush and the non-stop wonder of the song of the city you can hear if you listen the song and it stops

in some rare and sacred dead time, sandwiched between the late sleepers and the early risers, there is a miracle of silence.

Everything has stopped.

And silence drops down from out of the night, into this city, the briefest of silences, like a falter between heartbeats, like a darkness between blinks. Secretly, there is always this moment, an unexpected pause, a hesitation as one day is left behind and a new one begins.

by Jon McGregor

GRADE EIGHT – VERSE

My Rival

I go to concert, party, ball –
      What profit is in these?
I sit alone against the wall
      And strive to look at ease.
The incense that is mine by right
      They burn before Her shrine;
And that's because I'm seventeen
      And She is forty-nine.

I cannot check my girlish blush,
      My colour comes and goes.
I redden to my finger-tips,
      And sometimes to my nose.
But She is white where white should be,
      And red where red should shine.
The blush that flies at seventeen
      Is fixed at forty-nine.

I wish *I* had Her constant cheek;
      I wish that I could sing
All sorts of funny little songs,
      Not quite the proper thing.
I'm very *gauche* and very shy,
      Her jokes aren't in my line;
And, worst of all, I'm seventeen
      While She is forty-nine.

The young men come, the young men go,
      Each pink and white and neat,
She's older than their mothers, but
      They grovel at Her feet.
They walk beside Her 'rickshaw-wheels –
      None ever walk by mine;
And that's because I'm seventeen
      And She is forty-nine.

She rides with half a dozen men
      (She calls them 'boys' and 'mashes'),
I trot along the Mall alone;
      My prettiest frocks and sashes
Don't help to fill my programme-card,
      And vainly I repine
From ten to two a.m. Ah me!
      Would I were forty-nine.

She calls me 'darling,' 'pet,' and 'dear,'
      And 'sweet retiring maid.'
I'm always at the back, I know –
      She puts me in the shade.
She introduces me to men –
      'Cast' lovers, I opine;
For sixty takes to seventeen,
      Nineteen to forty-nine.

But even She must older grow
      And end Her dancing days,
She can't go on for ever so
      At concerts, balls, and plays.
One ray of priceless hope I see
      Before my footsteps shine;
Just think, that She'll be eighty-one
      When I am forty-nine!

by Rudyard Kipling

Digging

Between my finger and my thumb
The squat pen rests; snug as a gun.

Under my window, a clean rasping sound
When the spade sinks into gravelly ground:
My father, digging. I look down

Till his straining rump among the flowerbeds
Bends low, comes up twenty years away
Stooping in rhythm through potato drills
Where he was digging.

The coarse boot nestled on the lug, the shaft
Against the inside knee was levered firmly.
He rooted out tall tops, buried the bright edge deep
To scatter new potatoes that we picked
Loving their cool hardness in our hands.

By God, the old man could handle a spade.
Just like his old man.

My grandfather cut more turf in a day
Than any other man on Toner's bog.
Once I carried him milk in a bottle
Corked sloppily with paper. He straightened up
To drink it, then fell to right away

Nicking and slicing neatly, heaving sods
Over his shoulder, going down and down
For the good turf. Digging.

The cold smell of potato mould, the squelch and slap
Of soggy peat, the curt cuts of an edge
Through living roots awaken in my head.
But I've no spade to follow men like them.

Between my finger and my thumb
The squat pen rests.
I'll dig with it.

by Seamus Heaney

An Arundel Tomb

Side by side, their faces blurred,
The earl and countess lie in stone,
Their proper habits vaguely shown
As jointed armour, stiffened pleat,
And that faint hint of the absurd –
The little dogs under their feet.

Such plainness of the pre-baroque
Hardly involves the eye, until
It meets his left-hand gauntlet, still
Clasped empty in the other; and
One sees, with a sharp tender shock,
His hand withdrawn, holding her hand.

They would not think to lie so long.
Such faithfulness in effigy
Was just a detail friends would see:
A sculptor's sweet commissioned grace
Thrown off in helping to prolong
The Latin names around the base.

They would not guess how early in
Their supine stationary voyage
The air would change to soundless damage,
Turn the old tenantry away;
How soon succeeding eyes begin
To look, not read. Rigidly they

Persisted, linked, through lengths and breadths
Of time. Snow fell, undated. Light
Each summer thronged the glass. A bright
Litter of birdcalls strewed the same
Bone-riddled ground. And up the paths
The endless altered people came,
Washing at their identity.

Now, helpless in the hollow of
An unarmorial age, a trough
Of smoke in slow suspended skeins
Above their scrap of history,
Only an attitude remains:

Time has transfigured them into
Untruth. The stone fidelity
They hardly meant has come to be
Their final blazon, and to prove
Our almost-instinct almost true:
What will survive of us is love.

by Philip Larkin

Never Was Anything So Deserted

Never was anything so deserted
As this dim theatre
Now, when in passive grayness the remote
Morning is here,
Daunting the wintry glitter of the pale,
Half-lit chandelier.

Never was anything disenchanted
As this silence!
Gleams of soiled gilding on curved balconies,
Empty; immense
Dead crimson curtain, tasselled with its old
And staled pretence.

Nothing is heard but a shuffling and knocking
Of mop and mat,
Where dustily two charwomen exchange
Leisurely chat.
Stretching and settling to voluptuous sleep
Curls a cat.

The voices are gone, the voices
That laughed and cried.
It is as if the whole marvel of the world
Had blankly died,
Exposed, inert as a drowned body left
By the ebb of the tide.

Beautiful as water, beautiful as fire,
The voices came,
Made the eyes to open and the ears to hear,
The hand to lie intent and motionless,
The heart to flame,
The radiance of reality was there,
Splendour and shame.

Slowly an arm dropped, and an empire fell.
We saw, we knew.
A head was lifted, and a soul was freed.
Abysses opened into heaven and hell.
We heard, we drew
Into our thrilled veins courage of the truth
That searched us through.

But the voices are all departed,
The vision dull.
Daylight disconsolately enters
Only to annul.
The vast space is hollow and empty
As a skull.

by Laurence Binyon

Sarajevo

Bosnia. November. And the mountain roads
Earthbound but matching perfectly these long
And passionate self-communings counter-march,

Balanced on scarps of trap, ramble or blunder
Over traverses of cloud: and here they move,
Mule-teams like insects harnessed by a bell
Upon the leaf-edge of a winter sky.

And down at last into this lap of stone
Between four cataracts of rock: a town
Peopled by sleepy eagles, whispering only
Of the sunburnt herdsman's hopeless ploy:
A sterile earth quickened by shards or rock
Where nothing grows, not even in his sleep,

Where minarets have twisted up like sugar
And a river, curdled with blond ice, drives on
Tinkling among the mule-teams and the mountaineers,
Under the bridges and the wooden trellises
Which tame the air and promise us a peace
Harmless with nightingales. None are singing now.

No history much? Perhaps. Only this ominous
Dark beauty flowering under veils,
Trapped in the spectrum of a dying style:
A village like an instinct left to rust,
Composed around the echo of a pistol-shot.

by Lawrence Durrell

Siesta

Each day at this same hour
He comes to her
His lady of the afternoons.
Behind closed lids she hears the whispering brush-strokes
Gathering in the light, the windows and her sleeping form.
Her countenance is often in his dreams
But these are things not spoken of.
Outside the room where all this happens

In a splash of sunlight by the kitchen door
A maid trades amorous gossip with the gardener's boy
While shelling peas into her wide-spread lap;
A petal falls, someone puts out washing
And in the orchard among oranges
Her husband, whose idea it was,
Tends his bees, his face inside a net.
"I'm working on your mouth," the painter tells her.
She does not know his Christian name.
Her shut lids tremble. Just so
She used to close her eyes in childhood
Feigning sleep or death
Then open them in sudden laughter
To see her father's great moon face
Filling the everywhere;
Then later he was further off
And later still an absence
Like a place she took her heart to ache in.
Remembering this, she feels herself
Absorbed into the room
And in the darkness there
Beyond the limits of herself
Senses the painter with his canvas gone away
And lines of curious, reverential strangers
Filing past the open door
To gaze on her
Like one already dead.

by Gareth Owen

The Flea

Marke but this flea, and marke in this,
How little that which thou deny'st me is;
It suck'd me first, and now sucks thee,
And in this flea, our two bloods mingled bee;
Thou know'st that this cannot be said
A sinne, nor shame, nor losse of maidenhead,
    Yet this enjoyes before it wooe,
    And pamper'd swells with one blood made of two,
    And this, alas, is more than wee would doe.

Oh stay, three lives in one flea spare,
Where wee almost, yea more than maryed are.
This flea is you and I, and this
Our mariage bed, and mariage temple is;
Though parents grudge, and you, w'are met,
And cloysterd in these living walls of Jet.
    Though use make you apt to kill mee,
    Let not to that, selfe murder added bee,
    And sacrilege, three sinnes in killing three.

Cruell and sodaine, hast thou since
Purpled thy naile, in blood of innocence?
Wherein could this flea guilty bee,
Except in that drop which it suckt from thee?
Yet thou triumph'st, and saist that thou
Find'st not thy selfe, nor mee the weaker now;
    'Tis true, then learne how false, feares bee;
    Just so much honor, when thou yeeld'st to mee,
    Will wast, as this flea's death tooke life from thee.

by John Donne

Bat

At evening, sitting on this terrace,
When the sun from the west, beyond Pisa, beyond the
    mountains of Carrara
Departs, and the world is taken by surprise...

When the tired flower of Florence is in gloom beneath the
    glowing
Brown hills surrounding...

When under the arches of the Ponte Vecchio
A green light enters against stream, flush from the west,
Against the current of obscure Arno...

Look up, and you see things flying
Between the day and the night;
Swallows with spools of dark thread sewing the shadows
    together.

A circle swoop, and a quick parabola under the bridge arches
Where light pushes through;
A sudden turning upon itself of a thing in the air.
A dip to the water.

And you think:
"The swallows are flying so late!"

Swallows?

Dark air-life looping
Yet missing the pure loop...
A twitch, a twitter, an elastic shudder in flight
And serrated wings against the sky,
Like a glove, a black glove thrown up at the light,
And falling back.

Never swallows!
Bats!
The swallows are gone.

At a wavering instant the swallows gave way to bats
By the Ponte Vecchio...
Changing guard.

Bats, and an uneasy creeping in one's scalp
As the bats swoop overhead!
Flying madly.

Pipistrello!
Black piper on an infinitesimal pipe.
Little lumps that fly in air and have voices indefinite, wildly
    vindictive;

Wings like bits of umbrella.

Bats!

Creatures that hang themselves up like an old rag, to sleep;
And disgustingly upside down.

Hanging upside down like rows of disgusting old rags
And grinning in their sleep.
Bats!

Not for me!

By D H Lawrence

GRADE EIGHT – PROSE

The Kite Runner

After another thirty minutes, only four kites remained. And I was still flying. It seemed I could hardly make a wrong move, as if every gust of wind blew in my favour. I'd never felt so in command, so lucky. It felt intoxicating. I didn't dare look up to the roof. Didn't dare take my eyes off the sky. I had to concentrate, play it smart. Another fifteen minutes and what had seemed like a laughable dream that morning had suddenly become reality: It was just me and the other guy. The blue kite.

The tension in the air was as taut as the glass string I was tugging with my bloody hands. People were stomping their feet, clapping, whistling, chanting, *"Boboresh! Boboresh!" Cut him! Cut him!* I wondered if Baba's voice was one of them. Music blasted. The smell of steamed *mantu* and fried *pakora* drifted from rooftops and open doors.

But all I heard – all I willed myself to hear – was the thudding of blood in my head. All I saw was the blue kite. All I smelled was victory. Salvation. Redemption. If Baba was wrong and there *was* a God like they said in school, then He'd let me win. I didn't know what the other guy was playing for, maybe just bragging rights. But this was my one chance to become someone who was looked at, not seen, listened to, not heard. If there was a God, He'd guide the winds, let them blow for me so that, with a tug of my string, I'd cut loose my pain, my longing. I'd endured too much, come too far. And suddenly, just like that, hope became knowledge. I was going to win. It was just a matter of when.

It turned out to be sooner than later. A gust of wind lifted my kite and I took advantage. Fed the string, pulled up. Looped my kite on top of the blue one. I held position. The blue kite knew it was in trouble. It was trying desperately to maneuver out of the jam, but I didn't let go. I held position. The crowd sensed the end was at hand. The chorus of "Cut him! Cut him!" grew louder, like Romans chanting for the gladiators to kill, kill!

"You're almost there, Amir agha! Almost there!" Hassan was

panting.

Then the moment came. I closed my eyes and loosened my grip on the string. It sliced my fingers again as the wind dragged it. And then... I didn't need to hear the crowd's roar to know. I didn't need to see either. Hassan was screaming and his arm was wrapped around my neck.

"Bravo! Bravo, Amir agha!"

by Khaled Hosseini

Sense and Sensibility

A fond mother, though in pursuit of praise for her children the most rapacious of human beings, is likewise the most credulous; her demands are exorbitant; but she will swallow anything; and the excessive affection of the Miss Steeles towards her offspring were viewed therefore by Lady Middleton without the smallest surprise or distrust. She saw with maternal complacency all the impertinent incroachments and mischievous tricks to which her cousins submitted. She saw their sashes untied, their hair pulled about their ears, their work-bags searched, and their knives and scissors stolen away, and felt no doubt of it being a reciprocal enjoyment. It suggested no other surprise than that Elinor and Marianne should sit so composedly by, without claiming a share in what was passing.

"John is in such spirits today!" said she, on his taking Miss Steele's pocket handkerchief and throwing it out of the window. "He is full of monkey tricks."

And soon afterwards, on the second boy's violently pinching one of the same lady's fingers, she fondly observed, "How playful William is!"

"And here is my sweet little Annamaria," she added, tenderly caressing a little girl of three years old, who had not made a noise for the last two minutes; "And she is always so gentle and quiet. Never was there such a quiet little thing!"

But unfortunately in bestowing these embraces, a pin in her ladyship's head-dress, slightly scratching the child's neck, produced from this pattern of gentleness such violent screams as could hardly be outdone by any creature professedly noisy. The mother's consternation was excessive; but it could not surpass the alarm of the Miss Steeles, and everything was done by all three, in so critical an emergency, which affection could suggest as likely to assuage the agonies of the little sufferer. She was seated in her mother's lap, covered with kisses, her wound bathed with lavender-water, by one of the Miss Steeles, who was on her knees to attend her, and her mouth stuffed with sugar-plums by the other. With such a reward for her tears, the child was too wise to cease crying.

by Jane Austen

The City of Falling Angels

Suddenly, there was another earth-shaking boom. The roof over the backstage had fallen in.

A fire captain came up the stairs and told the Segusos, almost apologetically, that his men would have to run a hose through their living-room to a window facing the Fenice, just in case the fire breached the wall across the canal. But first the firemen cleared a path for the hose. With care verging on reverence, they moved Archimede Seguso's works of art in glass – the abstract, modernist pieces he had made in the 1920s and 1930s when most other Venetian glassmakers were still turning out flowery, eighteenth-century designs. When they laid down the fire hose, it was flanked by an honour guard of glass objects touched by Seguso's genius – bowls and vases embedded with fine threads of coloured glass resembling lace, or with undulating ribbons of colour, or with tiny bubbles suspended in rows and spirals. There were remarkable solid sculptures of people and animals made from single masses of molten glass, a seemingly impossible feat that he alone had mastered.

Gino came to his father's bedroom door accompanied by the fire captain. The captain, rather than presuming to address the old man directly, turned to Gino and said, "We are very concerned for the maestro's safety."

Signor Seguso continued to stare out the window in silence.

"Papa," said Gino in a gently pleading voice, "the fire is getting closer. I think we should leave."

Gino's father kept his eye on the Fenice, watching as bursts of green, purple, umber, and blue flames punctuated the fire. He could see the flames through the slits in the louvred shutters at the back of the Fenice, and he saw their reflections on the rippling puddles at the bottom of the canal. He saw great, long tongues of fire licking out through windows and geysers of glowing ash soaring through holes in the roof. The winter air outside the bedroom window had turned blazing hot. The Fenice had become a furnace.

"I'm staying here," Archimede Seguso said quietly.

by John Berendt

Cannery Row

The tide goes out imperceptibly. The boulders show and seem to rise up and the ocean recedes leaving little pools, leaving wet weed and moss and sponge, iridescence and brown and blue and China red. On the bottoms lie the incredible refuse of the sea, shells broken and chipped and bits of skeleton, claws, the whole sea bottom a fantastic cemetery on which the living scamper and scramble.

Doc pulled on his rubber boots and set his rain hat fussily. He took his buckets and jars and his crowbar and put his sandwiches in one pocket and his thermos bottle in another pocket and he went down the cliff to the tidal flat. Then he worked down the flat after the retreating sea. He turned over the boulders with his crowbar and now and then his hand darted quickly into the standing water and brought out a little angry squirming octopus which blushed with rage and spat ink on his hand. Then he dropped it into a jar of sea water with the others and usually the newcomer was so angry that it attacked its fellows.

It was good hunting that day. He got twenty-two little octopi. And he picked off several hundred sea cradles and put them in his wooden bucket. As the tide moved out he followed it while the morning came and the sun arose. The flat extended out two hundred yards and then there was a line of heavy weed-crusted rocks before it dropped off to deep water. Doc worked out to the barrier edge. He had about what he wanted now and the rest of the time he looked under stones, leaned down and peered into the tide pools with their brilliant mosaics and their scuttling, bubbling life. And he came at last to the outer barrier where the long leathery brown algae hung down into the water.

Red starfish clustered on the rocks and the sea pulsed up and down against the barrier waiting to get in again. Between two weeded rocks on the barrier Doc saw a flash of white under water and then the floating weed covered it. He climbed to the place over the slippery rocks, held himself firmly, and gently reached down and parted the brown algae. Then he grew rigid. A girl's face looked up at him, a pretty, pale girl with dark hair. The eyes were open and clear and the face was firm and the hair washed gently about her head. The body was out of sight, caught in the crevice. The lips were slightly parted and the teeth showed and on the face was only comfort and rest. Just under water it was and the clear water made it very beautiful. It seemed to Doc that he looked at it for many minutes, and the face burned into his picture memory.

by John Steinbeck

Arthur and George

Mrs Roberts stands there, slightly swaying, hands clasped together, head cast down. Every eye is upon her. Slowly, very slowly, she begins to lift her head; then her hands are unclasped and her arms begin to spread, while the slow sway continues. Finally, she speaks.

"There are vast numbers of spirits here with us," she begins. "They are pushing behind me like anything."

It does indeed seem like this: as if she is holding herself upright despite great pressure from several directions.

Nothing happens for a while, except more swaying, more unseen buffeting. The woman on George's right whispers, "She is waiting for Red Cloud to appear."

George nods.

"That's her spirit guide," the neighbour adds.

George does not know what to say. This is not his world at all.

"Many of the guides are Indians." The woman pauses, then smiles and adds, without the slightest embarrassment, "Red Indians, I mean."

The waiting is as active as the silence was; as if those in the hall are pressing upon the slim figure of Mrs Roberts much as any invisible spirits are. The waiting builds and the swaying figure plants her feet wider as if to hold her balance.

"They are pushing, they are pushing, many of them are unhappy, the hall, the lights, the world they prefer – a young man, dark hair brushed back, in uniform, a Sam Browne belt, he has a message – a woman, a mother, three children, one of them passed and is with her now – elderly gentleman bald head was a doctor not far from here a dark grey suit passed suddenly after a dreadful accident – a baby, yes, a little girl taken away by influenza she misses her two brothers Bob is one of them and her parents – Stop it! Stop it!" – Mrs Roberts suddenly shouts, and with her arms outstretched seems to push back at the spirits crowding behind her – "There are too many of them, their voices are confused, a middle-aged man in a dark overcoat who spent much of his life in Africa – he has a message – there is a white-haired grandmother who shares your anxiety and wants you to know –"

George listens to the crowd of spirits being given fleeting description. The impression is that they are all clamouring for attention, fighting to convey their messages. A facetious if logical question comes into George's mind, from where he cannot tell, unless as a reaction to all this unwonted intensity. If these are indeed the spirits of Englishmen and Englishwomen who have passed over into the next world, surely they would know how to form a proper queue?

by Julian Barnes

A Short History of Tractors in Ukranian

It all started with a phone call.

My father's voice, quavery with excitement, crackles down the line. "Good news, Nadezhda. I'm getting married!"

I remember the rush of blood to my head. Please let it be a joke! Oh, he's gone bonkers! Oh, you foolish old man! But I don't say any of those things. "Oh, that's nice, Pappa," I say.

"Yes, yes. She is coming with her son from Ukrania. Ternopil in Ukrania."

Ukrania: he sighs, breathing in the remembered scent of mown hay and cherry blossom. But I catch the distinct synthetic whiff of New Russia.

Her name is Valentina, he tells me. But she is more like Venus. "Botticelli's Venus rising from waves. Golden hair. Charming eyes. Superior breasts. When you see her you will understand."

The grown-up me is indulgent. How sweet – this last late

flowering of love. The daughter me is outraged. The traitor! And our mother barely two years dead. I am angry and curious. I can't wait to see her – this woman who is usurping my mother.

"She sounds *gorgeous*. When can I meet her?"

"After marriage you can meet."

"I think it might be better if we could meet her first, don't you?"

"Why you want to meet? You not marrying her." (He knows something's not quite right, but he thinks he can get away with it.)

"But Pappa, have you really thought this through? It seems very sudden. I mean, she must be a lot younger than you."

I modulate my voice very carefully, to conceal any signs of disapproval, like a worldly-wise adult dealing with a love-struck adolescent.

"Thirty-six. She's thirty-six and I'm eighty-four. So what?"

There is a snap in his voice. He has anticipated this question.

"Well, it's quite an age difference…"

"Nadezhda, I never thought you would be so bourgeois."

"No, no." He has me on the defensive. "It's just that… there could be problems."

by Marina Lewycka

The Fall of the House of Usher

I had taken but few turns in this manner, when a light step on an adjoining staircase arrested my attention. I presently recognized it as that of Usher. In an instant afterwards he rapped, with a gentle touch, at my door, and entered, bearing a lamp. His countenance was, as usual, cadaverously wan – but, moreover, there was a species of mad hilarity in his eyes – an evidently restrained *hysteria* in his whole demeanour. His air appalled me – but any thing was preferable to the solitude which I had so long endured, and I even welcomed his presence as a relief.

"And you have not seen it?" he said abruptly, after having stared about him for some moments in silence – "you have not then seen it? – but, stay! you shall." Thus speaking, and having carefully shaded his lamp, he hurried to one of the casements, and threw it freely open to the storm.

The impetuous fury of the entering gust nearly lifted us from our feet. It was, indeed, a tempestuous yet sternly beautiful night, and one wildly singular in its terror and its beauty. A whirlwind had apparently collected its force in our vicinity; for there were frequent and violent alterations in the direction of the wind; and the exceeding density of the clouds (which hung so low as to press upon the turrets of the house) did not prevent our perceiving the life-like velocity with which they flew careering from all points against each other, without passing away into the distance. I say that even their exceeding density did not prevent our perceiving this – yet we had no glimpse of the moon or stars, nor was there any flashing forth of the lightning. But the under surfaces of the huge masses of agitated vapour, as well as all terrestrial objects immediately around us, were glowing in the unnatural light of a faintly luminous and distinctly visible gaseous exhalation which hung about and enshrouded the mansion.

"You must not – you shall not behold this!" said I, shuddering, to Usher, as I led him, with a gentle violence, from the window to a seat. "These appearances, which bewilder you, are merely electrical phenomena not uncommon – or it may be that they have their ghastly origin in the rank miasma of the tarn. Let us close this casement; – the air is chilling and dangerous to your frame. Here is one of your favourite romances. I will read, and you shall listen: – and so we will pass away this terrible night together."

by Edgar Allan Poe

The Colour

Harriet stood by the wall of her garden, listening to the rain on her bean leaves. Then she turned and saw Joseph coming up towards her and knew that he had something to say, something which the longed-for rain had released in him.

He began by admiring the vegetable patch: the tiny stems of fruit on the currant bushes and the wine-coloured stalks of the beet tops. Then, he said: "I have made my decision. Now that the rain has come I can leave for a while and not worry that everything might die or fail. So, if you agree, I shall buy a boat passage to Nelson, then on to Hokitika."

Harriet stood very still, with the dog by her, with the moisture making silvery cobwebs in her hair. She didn't look at Joseph, but kept a watch on the earth, noting places where the rain didn't reach or where puddles were forming.

After a while, she bent down and stroked the dog's damp head, then straightened up and said: "And if I don't agree, what will you do?"

Joseph took off his hat and shook the rain from it and put it on again.

"I must go," he said. "I must go before all the gold is gone."

"And if there is no gold?"

"Men are not risking their lives for nothing, Harriet."

"Men are risking their lives *in the hope of something*. That is all."

"I have dreams about the Grey River. I shall come back with enough… enough gold to transform our world."

They were getting soaked, standing out there under the dark sky. Harriet hadn't minded this a moment ago, but now she saw how stupid it was; it was stupid because they were frail. "What have we been doing for all these months," she said, "but endeavouring to 'transform our world'?"

"Yes," said Joseph. "And we have. We have made the garden and the pond…"

"But you've lost heart in these things?"

Joseph hung his head. He didn't want to say that he'd lost heart in them on the morning in late winter when he'd first seen the colour at the creek's edge, that from that moment he'd begun to see them as small and of very little account. He reached out and tentatively took Harriet's hand. "I want more," he said.

by Rose Tremain

Publication Details of Prose Selections

Grade Two

Spid by Ursula Moray Williams, Anderson Press
(ISBN: 009940172X)
Harry's Mad by Dick King-Smith, Puffin
(ISBN: 0141302577)
A Handful of Horrid Henry by Francesca Simon, Orion
(ISBN: 1858818478)
The Owl who was Afraid of the Dark by Jill Tomlinson, Egmont
(ISBN: 9781405210935)
Shadow of the Minotaur by Alan Gibbons, Orion
(ISBN: 1858817218)
Molly Moon by Georgia Byng, Macmillan Children's Books
(ISBN: 0330399853)
The Snow Spider Trilogy by Jenny Nimmo, Egmont
(ISBN: 1405220104)
Alice in Wonderland by Lewis Carrol, Penguin Classics (ISBN: 9780141439761)

Grade Three

Artemis Fowl by Eoin Colfer, Puffin
(ISBN: 0141312122)
What Katy Did by Susan Coolidge, Wordsworth Editions Ltd
(ISBN: 9781853261312)
Smugglers by Christopher Russell, Puffin
(ISBN: 0141320958)
The Blue Roan Child by Jamieson Findlay, Chicken House
(ISBN: 0439627524)
Hitler's Canary by Sandi Toksvig, Corgi
(ISBN: 0440866626)
The Demon Headmaster by Gillian Cross, Puffin
(ISBN: 0140316434)
Here Lies Arthur by Phillip Reeve, Scholastic
(ISBN: 0439955335)
The Hundred-Mile-an-Hour Dog by Jeremy Strong, Puffin
(ISBN: 141322349)

Grade Four

Raven's Gate by Anthony Horowitz,
  Walker (ISBN: 1844286193)
Shadowmancer by G.P. Taylor,
  Faber & Faber (ISBN: 0571220460)
The Giver by Lois Lowry,
  Collins (ISBN: 0007141424)
The Wee Free Men by Terry Pratchett,
  Corgi (ISBN: 0552549053)
Chinese Cinderella by Adeline Yen Mah,
  Puffin (ISBN: 0141304871)
Out of the Ashes by Michael Morpurgo,
  Macmillan (ISBN: 0330400177)
The Diamond of Drury Lane by Julia Golding,
  Egmont (ISBN: 1405221496)
Wolf Brother by Michelle Paver,
  Orion (ISBN: 1842551310)

Grade Five

The No. 1 Ladies Detective Agency by Alexander McCall Smith,
  Abacus (ISBN: 034911675X)
Canterville Ghost by Oscar Wilde,
  Alan Rodgers Books (ISBN: 9781598188554)
Daughter of Venice by Donna Jo Napoli,
  Random House (ISBN: 074459059 0)
War Horse by Michael Morpurgo,
  Mammoth (ISBN: 0749704454)
The Ratcatcher by Roald Dahl,
  Penguin (ISBN: 0140118470)
Noughts and Crosses by Malorie Blackman,
  Corgi (ISBN: 0552555703)
I, Coriander by Sally Gardner,
  Orion (ISBN: 1842555049)
A Pack of Lies by Geraldine McCaughrean,
  Penguin (ISBN: 0140342761)

Grade Six

I am a cloud, I can blow anywhere by Jonathan & Shirley
   Tulloch, Egmont (ISBN: 1405223251)
The Life of Pi by Yann Martel,
   Canongate (ISBN: 184195392X)
Hullabaloo in the Guava Orchard by Kiran Desai,
   Faber & Faber (ISBN: 0571195717)
Eragon by Christopher Paolini,
   Corgi (ISBN: 0552552097)
Young Men in Spats by P G Wodehouse,
   Everyman's Library (ISBN: 1841591181)
The Lollipop Shoes by Joanne Harris,
   Doubleday (ISBN: 9780385609487)
The Withered Arm (from Wessex Tales) by Thomas Hardy,
   Oxford University Press (ISBN: 0192835580)
The Life & Times of The Thunderbolt Kid by Bill Bryson,
   Black Swan (ISBN: 0552772542)

Grade Seven

Great Expectations by Charles Dickens,
   Penguin (ISBN: 9781566194426)
The Other Side of the Dale by Gervase Phinn,
   Penguin (ISBN: 0140275428)
Cider with Rosie by James Roose-Evans,
   Vintage (ISBN: 0099285665)
Every Man for Himself by Beryl Bainbridge,
   Abacus (ISBN: 0349108706)
A Room with a View by E M Forster,
   Penguin (ISBN: 0141183292)
Tobermory (The Chronicles of Clovis) by Saki,
   The Echo Library (ISBN: 140680021X)
The Riddler's Gift by Greg Hamerton,
   Eternity Press (ISBN: 9780958511841)
If Nobody Speaks of Remarkable Things by John McGregor,
   Bloomsbury (ISBN: 0747561575)

Grade Eight

The Kite Runner by Khaled Hosseini,
   Bloomsbury (ISBN: 9780747566533)
The City of Falling Angels by John Berendt,
   Hodder & Stoughton (ISBN: 0340824980)
Cannery Row by John Steinbeck,
   Penguin (ISBN: 0141185082)
Sense and Sensibility by Jane Austen,
   Penguin (ISBN: 9780141439662)
Arthur & George by Julian Barnes,
   Jonathan Cape (ISBN: 0224675771)
A Short History of Tractors in Ukranian by Marina Lewycka,
   Penguin (ISBN: 0141034998)
The Fall of the House of Usher by Edgar Allan Poe,
   Signet Classics (ISBN: 9780451530318)
The Colour by Rose Tremain,
   Vintage (ISBN: 0099425157)

Title Index

Author Index

Acknowledgments

For permission to reprint the copyright material in the anthology we make grateful acknowledgment to the following authors, publishers and executors:

Adcock, Fleur *The Telephone Call* from Poems 1960-2000, used by permission of Bloodaxe Books.

Agard, John *Ask Mummy Ask Daddy* © 1998, published by Usborne Publishing, reproduced by kind permission of John Agard c/o Caroline Sheldon Literary Agency Limited.

Agard, John *The Hurt Boy and the Birds* © 1998, reproduced by kind permission of John Agard c/o Caroline Sheldon Literary Agency Limited.

Andrew, Moira *Lizard* used by permission of Moira Andrew.

Bainbridge, Beryl *Every Man for Himself* used by permission of Little, Brown Book Group Limited (UK | Commonwealth) and Johnson & Alcock (world).

Barnes, Julian *Arthur & George* published by Jonathan Cape, reprinted by permission of The Random House Group Ltd (UK | Europe | Commonwealth) and used by permission of PFD (World).

Bell, Anne *Assembly* from The Performer's Anthology published by Dramatic Lines used by permission of Triple D Books Publishing on behalf of Anne Bell.

Berry, James *When I Dance* is used by permission of PFD (www.pfd.co.uk) on behalf of James Berry.

Berendt, John *The City of Falling Angels* © 2005 published by High Water, Inc and used by permission of The Penguin Press, a division of Penguin Group USA Inc (US | Canada). Used by permission of Hodder (World).

Binyon, Laurence *Never Was Anything So Deserted* used by permission of The Society of Authors as the Literary Representative of the Estate of Laurence Binyon.

Blackman, Malorie *Noughts and Crosses* published by Doubleday, reprinted by permission of The Random House Group Ltd.

Bryson, Bill *The Life & Times of The Thunderbolt Kid* ©

2006 Bill Bryson, published by Black Swan, reprinted by permission of The Random House Group Ltd (UK | Europe | Commonwealth), Doubleday (Canada), Broadway Books - a division of Random House Inc (USA | Open Market) and Green & Heaton (World).

Byng, Georgia *Molly Moon* used by permission of Macmillan Children's Books London (UK) and by permission of HarperCollins Publishers (USA).

Calder, Dave *We Are Not Alone* from Read Me 1 published by Macmillan Children's Books, used by permission of Dave Calder.

Chisholm, Alison *Going Swimming* used by permission of Alison Chisholm.

Ciardi, John *About the Teeth of Sharks* used by permission of The Ciardi Family Trust.

Clark, Leonard *Twilight* from Is a Caterpillar Ticklish published by Puffin, used by permission of Leonard Clark.

Coldwell, John *When the Giant Comes to Breakfast* used by permission of John Coldwell.

Colfer, Eoin *Artemis Fowl* © 2001 published by Viking, used by permission of Penguin Books Ltd (UK) and Hyperion Books (World | USA | Canada).

Collett, Andrew *Story Time* from Poems about People published by Barefoot Books, reprinted by permission of Andrew Collett.

Coward, Noël Epitaph for an Elderly Actress from Noël Coward Collected Verse used by permission of Methuen Drama, an imprint of A&C Black Publishers.

Cowling, Sue *The Elephant Child* from What is a Kumquat? published by Faber & Faber, used by permission of Sue Cowling.

Cross, Gillian *The Demon Headmaster* © Gillian Cross 1982 published by Oxford University Press 2004, reprinted by permission of OUP.

Dahl, Roald *The Dentist and the Crocodile* from Rhyme Stew published by Jonathan Cape & Penguin Books Ltd, used by permission of David Higham Associates.

Dahl, Roald *The Rat Catcher* from Someone Like You

published by Penguin Books Ltd, used by permission of David Higham Associates.

De la Mare, Walter *Snow* used by permission of The Literary Trustees of Walter de la Mare and The Society of Authors as their representative.

Desai, Kiran *Hullabaloo in the Guava Orchard* © 1998 Kiran Desai, used by permission of Faber & Faber Ltd (UK | Commonwealth | Europe) and Grove/Atlantic Inc. (USA | Canada | Open Market).

Dharker, Imtiaz *The Right Word* © 2006 from The Terrorist at my table, used by permission of Bloodaxe Books.

Dixon, Peter *Magic Cat* from Peter Dixon's Grand Prix of Poetry, used by permission of Macmillan Children's Books, London.

Doherty, Berlie *Night Sounds* from Walking on Air published by Hodder, used by permission of David Higham Associates.

Durrell, Lawrence *Sarajevo* © 1951 Lawrence Durrell, used by permission of Curtis Brown Group Ltd, London on behalf of the Estate of Lawrence Durrell.

Edwards, Richard *The Wizard Said:* from Whispers from the Wardrobe, used by permission of The Lutterworth Press.

Emery, Jacqueline *Jungle Piece* and *Football* used by permission of Jacqueline Emery.

Fanthorpe. U A *Mother-in-Law* © 2005 from Collected Poems 1978–2003, used by permission of Peterloo Poets.

Farjeon, Eleanor *There are Big Waves* from The Puffin Book of Fantastic First Poems published by Puffin, used by permission of David Higham Associates Ltd.

Fatchen, Max *Tailpiece* used by permission of Johnson & Alcock Ltd.

Fatchen, Max *Ears* from Wry Rhymes for Troublesome Times used by permission of Johnson & Alcock Ltd.

Findlay, Jamieson *The Blue Roan Child* © 2002 used by permission of Chicken House Publishing Ltd (UK). Reprinted by permission of Doubleday (Canada).

Forster, E M *A Room with a View* used by permission of The Society of Authors Literary Estates.

Foster, John *Tastes* used by permission of John Foster.

Fried, Erich *Conversation with a Survivor* from Being Alive © John Calder Publishers Ltd and the Estate of Eric Fried 1991; translation © Stuart Hood 1991, used with permission.

Frost, Robert *House Fear* from The Poetry of Robert Frost edited by Edward Connery Lathem. © 1916, 1969 Henry Holt and Company, © 1944 by Robert Frost. Reprinted by permission of Henry Holt and Company (USA | Canada). Published by Jonathan Cape, reprinted by permission of Random House Group Ltd (UK | Commonwealth).

Gardner, Sally *I, Coriander* used by permission of Orion Children's Books.

Gibbons, Alan *Shadow of the Minotaur* used by permission of Orion Children's Books.

Golding, Julia *The Diamond of Drury Lane* published by Egmont and used by permission of David Higham Associates.

Gowar, Mick *Christmas Thank Yous* used by permission of Penrose Literary Agency.

Gray, Nigel *Summing Up* used by permission of Nigel Gray.

Hamerton, Greg *The Riddler's Gift* © 2007 published by Eternity Press Ltd (www.eternity-press.com) and used by permission of the author.

Harris, Joanne *The Lollipop Shoes* published by Doubleday and reprinted by permission of The Random House Group Ltd (World). From The Girl with no Shadow published by Frogspawn © 2008 and reprinted by permission of HarperCollins Publishers (USA).

Heaney, Seamus *Digging* from Death of a Naturalist used by permission of Faber & Faber Ltd (UK). © 1988 Seamus Heaney from Opened Ground: Selected Poems 1966-1996, reprinted by permission of Farrar, Strauss & Giroux (USA).

Hesketh, Phoebe *Yew Tree Guest House* from The Leave Train: New and Selected Poems © 1994 used by permission of Enitharmon Press on behalf of the Estate of Phoebe Hesketh.

Horowitz, Anthony *The Power of 5: Raven's Gate* © 2005

Anthony Horowitz, published by Scholastic Inc./Scholastic Press and reprinted with permission (USA | Canada). Text © Stormbreaker Productions Ltd reproduced by permission of Walker Books Ltd, London SE11 5HJ (UK | World).

Hosseini, Khaled *The Kite Runner* © 2003 Khaled Hosseini published by Bloomsbury and used with permission (UK). Reprinted by permission of Riverhead Books, an imprint of Penguin Group USA Inc (USA), and Doubleday Canada (Canada).

Hughes, Ted *Full Moon and Little Frieda* © 1962 from Uncollected Poems published by Turret Books, London. Appeared in the Hudson Review. Used by permission of HarperCollins (USA) and Faber & Faber (UK | World).

Ireson, Barbara *The Small Ghostie* from Rhyme Time 2 published by Red Fox and reprinted by permission of The Random House Group Ltd.

Ireson, Barbara *Star-trip* from Spaceman, Spaceman published by Picture Corgi, reprinted by permission of The Random House Group Ltd.

Jennings, Elizabeth *Remember* from A Spell of Words published by Macmillan, used by permission of the author c/o David Higham Associates.

King-Smith, Dick *Harry's Mad* © 1984 Dick King-Smith, illustrations copyright Jill Bennett. Used by permission of Random House Children's Books, a division of Random House, Inc. (USA). Used by permission of A P Watt Ltd on behalf of Dick-King Smith (World).

Kirkup, James *Sand Artist* from The Orchard Book of Poems edited by Adrian Mitchell, used by permission of James Kirkup.

Kretzmer, Herbert *Monkey* used by permission of Berlin Associates Ltd.

Kuskin, Karla *Tiptoe* © 1959 renewed 1986 by Karla Kuskin, used by permission of S©ott Treimel NY.

Larkin, Philip *An Arundel Tomb* from Collected Poems by Philip Larkin © 1988, 2003 The Estate of Philip Larkin. Reprinted by permission of Farrar, Straus and Giroux LLC (USA | Open market) and Faber & Faber UK Ltd (UK).

reprinted with permission.

McGough, Roger *The Sound Collector* © 1990 from Pillow Talk, used by permission of PFD (www.pfd.co.uk) on behalf of Roger McGough.

McGregor, John *If Nobody Speaks of Remarkable Things* © 2002 Jon McGregor published by Bloomsbury Publishing PLC and used with permission (UK | Commonwealth). Used by permission of The Wylie Agency London (USA).

McLeod, Eleanor *Storm* from Poems For Children To Enjoy published by Exposure Publishing, used by permission of Eleanor McLeod.

McLeod, Eleanor *A Fierce Pirate Crew* used by permission of Eleanor McLeod.

McMillan, Ian *Sock Song* used by permission of Adrian Mealing on behalf of www.ian-mcmillan.co.uk.

Mitton, Tony *Grown out of* © 2006 from My Hat And All That published by Corgi, used by permission of David Higham Associates.

Mitton, Tony *Dreaming the Unicorn* from 101 Favourite Poems used by permission of David Higham Associates.

Mordecai, Pamela *Remember* from Story Poems: A First Collection published by Walker Books, used by permission of Pearson Education.

Morpurgo, Michael *Out of the Ashes* published by Macmillan Children's Books, used by permission of David Higham Associates.

Morpurgo, Michael *War Horse* used by permission of David Higham Associates.

Mortimer, Peter *Babies are Boring* from Utter Nonsense, used by permission of Iron Press.

Napoli, Donna Jo *Daughter of Venice* © 2002 Donna Jo Napoli, used by permission of Random House Children's Books, a division of Random House, Inc.

Nimmo, Jenny *The Snow Spider Trilogy* published by Egmont, used by permission of David Higham Associates.

Noyes, Alfred *The Highwayman Part One* used by permission of The Society of Authors as the Literary Representatives of the Estate of Alfred Noyes (UK).

pfd.co.uk) on behalf of Michael Rosen (World).

Rush, Philip R *Mirage* from Australian Outback Poems, used by permission of Philip R Rush.

Russell, Christopher *Smugglers* © 2007 published by Puffin Books, used by permission of Penguin Books Ltd.

Simon, Francesca *A Handful of Horrid Henry* used by permission of Orion Children's Books. Horrid Henry is a registered trademark.

Somjee, Shehnaz *The Street Healer of Karachi* used by permission of Shehnaz Somjee.

Spender, Stephen *Dolphins* © 2004 from New Collected Poems by Stephen Spender, reprinted by kind permission of the Estate of Stephen Spender.

Steinbeck, John *Cannery Row* © 1945 John Steinbeck renewed © 1973 by Elaine Steinbeck, John Steinbeck IV and Thom Steinbeck. Used by permission of Viking Penguin, a division of Penguin Group USA Inc (USA | Canada). Published by Michael Joseph 1988 and used by permission of Penguin Books Ltd (World).

Stevens, Roger *Escape Plan* © 2004 from The Monster That Ate The Universe published by Macmillan Children's Books and used by permission of Roger Stevens.

Stickland, Paul & Henrietta *Dinosaur Roar* © 1999 illustrated by Paul Stickland and published by Ragged Bears Ltd, used by permission of Henrietta Stickland.

Strong, Jeremy *The Hundred-Mile-an-Hour Dog* published by Puffin, used by permission of the author c/o David Higham Associates.

Sweeney, Matthew *Spotlight* from Fatso in the Red Suit, used by permission of Faber and Faber.

Swenson, May *Water Picture* © 1994 from Nature: Poems Old and New, used by permission of The Literary Estate of May Swenson c/o Houghton Mifflin Harcourt Publishing.

Taylor, G P *Shadowmancer* © 2002 G P Taylor reproduced by kind permission of G P Taylor c/o Caroline Sheldon Literary Agency Limited (World). Used by permission of Faber & Faber Ltd (UK | Commonwealth but not Canada | Europe).